INSTRUCTOR'S MANUAL AND TEST BANK

The Blue Planet

An Introduction to Earth System Science

Brian J. Skinner
Yale University

Stephen C. Porter
University of Washington

Barbara Murck
University of Toronto

John Wiley & Sons, Inc.

New York   Chichester   Brisbane   Toronto   Singapore

CONTENTS

ABOUT THE MANUAL

PURPOSE

This manual is intended to serve as a guide for instructors adopting the textbook *The Blue Planet* by Brian J. Skinner and Stephen C. Porter. Other publisher's supplements also accompany *The Blue Planet;* they are described on page v of the text.

It was my intention to create a manual that would be of assistance to both new and experienced teachers of Earth science courses. The primary purpose of the manual is to facilitate your teaching, and to enable you to make the fullest possible use of the materials presented in the text. To that end, the manual offers organizational and pedagogical information about the text, as well as a wide range of suggestions for readings, audiovisuals, and other resources that may help you to enrich your students' classroom experiences.

ORGANIZATION

The manual first provides an overview of the text: its goals, its underlying philosophy, and its organization. Then each part and chapter of the book is briefly summarized in turn. This is followed by three possible course syllabi and organizational schemes, with suggestions for resources to assist in the presentation of specific topics. The remainder of the materials in the manual (audio-visual resources, computer resources, etc.) have been presented in integrated lists, rather than chapter-by-chapter. The reason for adopting this organizational plan is simple: in Earth System Science the focus is on integration, rather than segregation. All parts of the Earth system are interrelated, and it is difficult to separate or compartmentalize them; it is equally difficult to compartmentalize the resources related to the teaching of Earth System Science.

LET'S COMMUNICATE

We are interested in opening lines of communication among the users of *The Blue Planet*, the publisher, the authors, and other contributors. If you have comments concerning any of the ideas or resources suggested in this manual, or any additional resources you might want to recommend, contact: Barbara Murck, Department of Earth Science, Erindale College, University of Toronto, Mississauga, Ontario L5L 1C6 Canada. If you have comments concerning *The Blue Planet*, contact the editor: Chris Rogers, College Division, John Wiley & Sons, 605 Third Avenue, New York, NY 10158-0012. If you have comments concerning any of the supplementary materials, contact the supplements editor: Eric Stano, College Division, John Wiley & Sons. Perhaps we can work together to enhance and facilitate the teaching of Earth System Science.

ABOUT THE BOOK

OBJECTIVES

Earth System Science is rapidly changing the way we study and think about the Earth, and as a result it is changing the way Earth Science courses are being taught. Courses about the Earth are being taught with increasing frequency. Such courses may have titles such as Global Change, Earth Science, Biospherics, or even The Global Environment, but the approach is increasingly that of Earth System Science.

This book is intended to be an introduction to the holistic view of the Earth. It is about the interactions between the different parts of the Earth—the atmosphere, hydrosphere, biosphere, and the solid Earth—and about the balance in the global environment that exists as a result of those interactions. One of the discoveries that arise from the holistic view of the Earth is that our modern industrial society and our huge population are changing the Earth; the impacts of human activities on the Earth system is a special focus of the book.

ORGANIZATION

The text begins with a discussion of the Earth's place in the solar system, in *Part One: The Earth In Space.* The Earth's appearance and structure are contrasted with those of neighboring planetary bodies. A chapter is devoted to the Sun, not only because it is the dominant feature of the solar system, but because it supplies the energy that drives most of the surface processes on our planet and that permits life to exist.

Part Two: The Earth Beneath Our Feet introduces the solid Earth, the minerals and rocks that comprise it, the nature of processes operating deep within the Earth that are inferred indirectly, and the dynamics of the crust that are explained in terms of a relatively new, comprehensive theory, the theory of plate tectonics.

Having explored the solid Earth, the authors next examine the layers of water and ice that cover much of its surface in *Part Three: The Earth's Blanket of Water and Ice.* This section encompasses the oceans, streams, groundwater, snow, glaciers, sea ice, and frozen ground, and explores how some of these different agents erode and shape landscapes on which we live.

In the next part of the book, *Part Four: The Earth's Gaseous Envelope,* the atmosphere, weather, and climate are explored, and evidence of past changes in climate are examined.

Having discussed the aspects of the Earth that have made it a habitable planet, the authors next turn to the diversity and dynamics of plants and animals comprising the biosphere and the evidence of biological evolution through Earth history that is recorded in fossiliferous rocks, in *Part Five: The Dynamics of Life on Earth.*

In the final section of the book, *Part Six: Living on the Earth,* the authors look at natural resources that have permitted the development and growth of modern civilization, and ways in which human activities contribute to global changes in our environment.

PEDAGOGICAL FEATURES

The key to understanding the Earth system is an appreciation of the interactions between the spheres. Interactions are emphasized by icons, each of which represents a part of the system. The icons appear throughout the book and help the reader identify sections in the text where interactions are discussed.

Each of the parts of the book opens with a brief essay on a special aspect of the topics covered within the chapters of the part. The intent of the part-opening essays is to emphasize that the different parts of the Earth system are interdependent. Each of the chapters in the book also opens with a topical essay dealing with research on the chapter topic. Within the chapters, specialized and detailed topics are boxed under the heading *A Closer Look.* Inclusion or deletion of the boxed material can be at the discretion of the instructor.

Each chapter closes with a guest essay written by a researcher in the field. The essay subjects relate directly to material in the chapter and are intended to provide insights into on-going research. Finally, each chapter closes with a summary of in-chapter material, a list of key terms, and questions. The questions are of two kinds: first, review questions relating strictly to the material in the chapter; second, discussion questions, which are intended for class or section discussion, sometimes call for a bit of library research, and in most cases raise broader issues than those in the specific chapter to which they are attached.

A comprehensive Glossary of terms is included at the end of the text. The appendices are: Appendix A: Units and Their Conversions; Appendix B: The Periodic Table of the Elements; Appendix C: Seasonal Star Charts; Appendix D: World Soils and Soil Classification System; Appendix E: The Köppen Climatic Classification System; and Appendix F: Topographic Maps.

(adapted from *Preface* to *The Blue Planet*)

CHAPTER SYNOPSES

In these brief chapter synopses I have included some editorial remarks *[in brackets and italics, like this]* with suggestions for specific topics, organizational approaches, or examples that you might want to employ in your lectures. Other instructional resources, such as slides, videos, etc., are suggested in the sample course syllabi and in the lists of Resources provided in other sections of this manual.

INTRODUCTION

SYNOPSIS/LECTURE LEAD-IN

[The Introduction is a very important part of this book, in which many fundamental principles are brought forth; don't let your students skip reading it!]

What is Earth System Science? It is the science that studies the whole Earth as a system of many interacting parts, and focuses on the changes within and between these parts (p. 4). The goal of Earth System Science is to present a holistic view of the Earth. Throughout *The Blue Planet,* the Earth system is considered in terms of four great interacting reservoirs, with flows of matter and energy between them (p. 5). These reservoirs are the atmosphere, the hydrosphere, the biosphere, and the solid Earth.

Earth System Science, like the individual sciences that contribute to it (chemistry, physics, biology, geology, etc.), is based on the scientific method (p. 4). The scientific method is a time-tested approach to learning about and understanding the natural world. It involves the observation, examination, and re-examination of scientific evidence, with the goal of producing hypotheses and, eventually, devising laws about the way the natural world functions.

The Introduction begins with an example of interactions among different parts of the Earth system—the example of the impacts of great volcanic eruptions on global climate (p. 3). There are lots of other examples that illustrate interactions among Earth systems. *[For example: El Niño is an ocean current phenomenon involving anomalously warm seawater temperatures off the western coast of South America. During an El Niño event, trade winds in the equatorial region off the coast of South America weaken or even reverse their direction. The winds, currents, and seawater temperature all interact with one another during such an event, but the exact triggering phenomenon and timing of El Niño events are still unclear. It has even been suggested that submarine volcanic activity may cause water temperature anomalies, which could be sufficient to generate anomalous currents, ultimately leading to an El Niño event. The unusually warm waters of El Niño cause large shifts in biota, as well as causing dramatic changes in weather (such as droughts or heavy rains) in many parts of the world. An El Niño event is truly a process in which all parts of the Earth system—atmosphere, hydrosphere, biosphere, and solid Earth—interact and affect one another. El Niño is discussed in further detail in Chapter 8, pp. 207-208.]*

Where does the energy come from that drives the flow of matter and energy among the interacting parts of the Earth system (pp. 12-15)? There are three main sources: the Sun, the interior of the Earth, and the tides. Energy from the Sun, with a small contribution from tidal energy, drives all of the Earth's external processes, such as rain, wind, streams, waves, currents, and even glaciers. Energy from the Earth's interior is responsible, through the process of plate tectonics, for shaping the surface of the Earth, building mountains, triggering earthquakes, and causing volcanic eruptions. The Earth's surface is an especially dynamic place to live because it is the interface where the processes driven by these two great energy sources—the Sun and from the Earth's interior—meet and interact.

Much of what we study in Earth System Science is based on Hutton's Principle of Uniformitarianism (pp. 7-10). Uniformitarianism is the concept that the present is the key to the understanding the past, and that the processes we observe in the natural world today have operated in much the same way (although sometimes on different temporal or spatial scales) throughout most of Earth history. If we stand back far enough and take a broad view of the Earth as a planet in the context of our solar system and our galaxy, even catastrophic events like meteorite impacts can be seen to fit into a uniformitarian view of Earth history.

An important part of Earth System Science is to recognize the impacts of the ever-growing human population on the functioning of natural systems (pp. 11-12). We have even coined a special term to describe the changes produced in the Earth system as a result of human activities: global change. Measuring, monitoring, and understanding global change is now a topic of intense study by many scientists.

PART ONE
The Earth in Space

SYNOPSIS/LECTURE LEAD-IN

A fundamental aspect of the systems approach to Earth science is the view of Earth as a planet in the context of our solar system. We are at home in the solar system because our planet was formed by the same set of processes by which the other planets originated. The Earth also has many features in common with other planets, particularly the other "terrestrial" or Earth-like planets. Yet Earth is different from the other planets and unique in many respects—most importantly, in its ability to host life. We should keep both similarities and differences between Earth and the other planets in perspective as we begin our exploration of the Earth system.

[It is worth noting that, in the annals of powerful images, the first photograph of the Earth taken from outer space must surely rank as one of the most significant. Our first look at "spaceship Earth" changed our view of our home planet forever. In this image, for the first time, we saw a planet among others, with limited resources, a particularly fragile-looking atmospheric envelope, and an extraordinary set of physical characteristics rendering it both hospitable to life and vulnerable to the impacts of the dominant species: Humankind.]

Venus and Earth, in particular, started out very much alike: almost the same size, comparable distance from the Sun, similar in bulk composition and density (pp. 20-21). Yet today the surface of Venus is hot enough to melt lead, drenched in a carbon dioxide-dominated atmosphere heavy with sulfuric acid clouds. Why have these twin sister planets evolved along such different paths? *[You might want to leave the answer to this question dangling until later in the term, or refer back to the question later on, after you have talked about the greenhouse effect and the evolution of the atmosphere, hydrosphere, and biosphere.]* The answer to this question has to do with the chemical evolution of the Earth's atmosphere and hydrosphere and, in particular, the influence of life on this process. On the Earth, plants and other organisms in the biosphere remove carbon dioxide released into the atmosphere by volcanoes. Living organisms incorporate carbon as carbon dioxide in limestone or as organic matter buried in rocks. Because Venus lacks a biosphere, all of its carbon dioxide remains in the atmosphere.

CHAPTER 1
Fellow Travellers: Earth's Nearest Neighbors

SYNOPSIS/LECTURE LEAD-IN

[When I lecture about the Earth in the context of the solar system, I often begin with a "tour of the solar system," seen through the eyes of an imaginary extraterrestrial visitor. The space program has produced so many strikingly beautiful images of planets in our solar system; a "tour" is a good vehicle for introducing students to a wide variety of images.]

What would an extraterrestrial visitor see on a tour of the planets in our solar system? What features of the third planet from the Sun would immediately strike the visitor as unique or significant? In what ways is the Earth similar to the other planets? In what ways is it different or unique? Why is Earth—but not any of the other planets in the solar system—hospitable to life?

There are nine planets in our solar system, along with a wide variety of other bodies, including ring systems; satellites (moons) orbiting the planets; comets; and asteroids. All of them are governed by the basic laws of physics and astronomy, of which the most important are Kepler's Laws of Planetary Motion (pp. 26-27) and Newton's Law of Gravitation (pp. 28-29). Our solar system formed when a rotating cloud of gas and dust—the solar nebula—collapsed in on itself (pp. 30-31). When the core of this collapsing cloud became dense enough and hot enough, it "ignited" nuclear reactions, and a star (our Sun) was born. Solids that condensed out of the cooler parts of the nebula eventually became the planets, moons, and other objects in the solar system.

The planets can be separated into two groups based on density and closeness to the Sun (pp. 33-34). The innermost planets—Mercury, Venus, Earth, and Mars—are called the terrestrial planets, because they are all small, rocky, and dense, similar in many respects to the Earth. The outermost planets (with the exception of Pluto) are all much larger and much less dense than the terrestrial planets. These planets—Jupiter, Saturn, and Neptune—are collectively called the jovian planets. The physical and orbital characteristics and spatial distribution of materials that make up the planets of the solar system—from the rocky inner planets to the icy and gaseous outer planets—are the legacy of the processes that were originally responsible for the condensation of materials in the solar nebula and the formation of the planets. The terrestrial planets (pp. 35-38) are characterized by concentric layers of differing composition, rock strength, and physical state. The jovian planets, by contrast (pp. 38-39), are gas giants (with the exception of the odd-ball Pluto), consisting of huge, low-density masses, probably with small, rocky or icy cores.

[In contemplating the impacts of human activities on the Earth system, it is interesting to note that—given the absence of an atmosphere or hydrosphere, and consequently the absence of any erosional processes on the Moon—the footprints of the astronauts who walked on the Moon will remain visible in the lunar regolith for millions of years!]

CHAPTER 2
The Sun, Giver of Life

SYNOPSIS/LECTURE LEAD-IN

Our Sun—even though it seems fundamentally important and unique to us—is really just an ordinary, medium-sized, middle-aged star, one among billions like it in the Milky Way Galaxy and the other galaxies of the universe (p. 46). It makes good sense for us to begin our study of the Earth system by looking at the Sun and its characteristics, for three reasons:

(1)   the Sun is the center of our solar system;
(2)   many of the Earth's unique characteristics (especially the ability to support life and the presence of water in three forms—solid, liquid, and vapor—at the Earth's surface) exist by virtue of the Earth's special relationship with the Sun (distance, orbital characteristics, etc.); and
(3)   energy from the Sun is responsible for driving most of the Earth's external processes, including rain, wind, snow, currents, waves, and others.

The Sun's energy comes from nuclear reactions in its core (pp. 49-51). The Sun's energy reaches the surface of the Earth in the form of electromagnetic radiation, a whole spectrum of waves travelling at the same velocity but different wavelengths and frequencies (pp. 50-51). The most familiar type of electromagnetic radiation is visible light, but there are lots of others (including microwave radiation, x-rays, and radio waves, among others).

The Sun is an extremely active body. Some of the activity going on inside the Sun involves changes in the photosphere, the turbulent outer layer of the Sun (pp. 51-52, 55-56). Changes also occur in the Sun's luminosity, the total amount of energy being radiated from the Sun (or any other star, for that matter) each second (p. 57). These changes in the Sun have impacts on the Earth's climate, but the exact nature and extent of the impacts is not well understood.

The nuclear processes responsible for energy production in the Sun are the same as the processes at work in countless other stars in our galaxy and elsewhere in the universe. For this reason, we can study the Sun using the same techniques we use to study other stars. In particular, it is instructive to consider the life cycles of stars with respect to their different masses and luminosities, for which we utilize a tool called a Hertzsprung-Russell diagram (pp. 59-65). The life cycles of stars are so much longer than human lifetimes that we can only decipher them by relying on the Principle of Uniformitarianism: we must assume that the processes of star formation, evolution, and death that we observe today have operated throughout much of the history of the universe.

PART TWO
The Earth Beneath Our Feet

SYNOPSIS/LECTURE LEAD-IN

The history of Earth science is the history of peoples' efforts to explain how the Earth works and why the Earth's surface looks the way it does (p. 68). Why are there volcanoes, and why do they occur where they do? What causes earthquakes? What forces are responsible for the formation of high mountains? Why is there such a sharp distinction between the high-standing continents and the low-lying ocean basins? How come some of the continental coastlines seem to fit neatly together, almost like the pieces of a giant puzzle? And why do we find the remains of rocks and creatures that obviously formed in the ocean, on the summits of high mountains? These and other questions about Earth processes have occupied natural scientists for centuries—perhaps since the dawn of scientific inquiry, as suggested by this ancient quote attributed to Seneca (4 B.C. - 65 A.D.):

It is useful to be assured that the heavings of the Earth are not the work of angry deities; these phenomena have causes of their own.

Throughout the years, many grand hypotheses have been proposed to explain the Earth's features. One of the longest-lived of these was the theory of catastrophism *[described in greater detail in the Introduction, pp. 7-10]*, in which massive, catastrophic events like the biblical flood were responsible for carving out the features of the Earth's surface and scattering the remains of marine creatures over all parts of the globe. The realization that the Earth's interior is hot led to many hypotheses concerning the effects of contraction and expansion of the Earth on its outer shell (p. 68). But none of these hypotheses satisfactorily explained all the observed features of the Earth's surface.

Then, in the mid-1960s, the science of geology underwent a "scientific revolution," which led to the development of a unified theory. This theory—which we now call the theory of plate tectonics—provides an explanation, a unified framework, and a model for the major features of the Earth's surface, and answers many of the questions posed above. The theory of plate tectonics is now subscribed to by most—but not all—Earth scientists *[see Guest Essay, p. 187]*.

CHAPTER 3
Earthquakes and the Earth's Interior

SYNOPSIS/LECTURE LEAD-IN

The occurrence of an earthquake is an obvious sign—obvious, at least, to people who live in seismically active zones—that the Earth is very active internally. In a matter of seconds, earthquakes can cause death and disaster over large regions; the example in the text cites the 1976 earthquake at T'ang Shan, China, in which 240,000 people were killed (p. 71). Charles Darwin, in a quote that now seems amazingly prescient of the theory of plate tectonics and the discovery of the aesthenosphere, wrote about his experiences with earthquakes:

> *A bad earthquake at once destroys the oldest associations; the world, the very emblem of all that is solid, had moved beneath our feet like crust over fluid; one second of time has created in the mind a strange idea of insecurity, which hours of reflection would not have produced. (1835, Concepción, Chile)*

Earthquakes occur when two rock masses are moving past one another along a fault. If the masses lock against one another instead of slipping easily, strain energy builds up and the rocks undergo elastic deformation. When slip finally occurs, the deformed rocks will rebound, returning to their original shapes while releasing an enormous amount of energy in the form of an earthquake (p. 72). *[One way to demonstrate elastic deformation and rebound is with a wooden yardstick. Lay the yardstick across the edge of a table, with about two-thirds of it sticking over the edge. Press down slowly on the free end of the yardstick, bending it as far as you can without breaking it. Then release the yardstick suddenly, and it will bounce back to its original position.]*

The energy released during an earthquake travels in the form of seismic waves (pp. 73-75). Body waves, which travel through the Earth's interior, may be compressional/expansional waves (P waves, pp. 73-74) or shear waves (S waves, pp. 74-75). Shear waves have the important property that they cannot be transmitted through fluids. Surface waves are seismic waves that travel along the outer surface of the Earth (p. 75). *[The classic way to demonstrate seismic waves is to use a loose spring, such as a Slinky®. A traffic jam is also a good analogy for a compressional wave.]*

Although they are responsible for much human suffering, earthquakes have been extremely useful in furthering our scientific understanding of the Earth. The study of the behavior of seismic waves as they pass through the Earth has been the single most important source of information about the physical properties of the Earth's interior (pp. 73-77). From these studies, scientists have determined that the Earth has an inner core, a fluid outer core, and layers of differing physical properties separated by discontinuities. *[You can demonstrate the seismic shadow zone (Fig. 3.6 in the text) by cutting a large circle out of construction paper or poster board. Place the circle flat on the table and place an obstacle, such as a large coffee can, in the center of the circle. Shine a flashlight from one edge of the circle to the other. At the opposite side of the circle the light will be blocked by the can, forming a shadow zone. Connect the point marking the position of the flashlight with the points marking the two edges of the shadow zone. If you repeat this exercise several times, and then remove the can, you will see the shape of the can (analogous to the outer core), revealed by the lines you have drawn.]*

CHAPTER 4
Minerals and Rocks

SYNOPSIS/LECTURE LEAD-IN

There are three main reasons why it is important to include the study of minerals and rocks in a study of the Earth system:

(1)   rocks and minerals are the building blocks of the Earth;
(2)   rocks and minerals are important resources; and
(3)   the physical and chemical properties of rocks and minerals affect both human activities and the workings of natural Earth systems.

For example, it is important that we understand the properties of a mineral like asbestos that is used in our built environment. We need to understand the properties of clay minerals, because they can be important in absorbing chemical wastes disposed of underground. Certain rocks and minerals may have properties that give them a tendency to fail under certain circumstances, leading to landslides. Others may be important as hosts for oil, or water, or ore deposits.

Minerals are made of chemical elements (p. 92) *[I find that this material is often very challenging for students suffering from "science paranoia," but careful use of familiar examples will assist them in mastering these concepts.]* An example of a chemical element is sodium. The smallest piece of material with all the properties of that material is called an atom. Atoms combine into chemical compounds (p. 93). An example of a chemical compound is the combination of sodium and chloride (NaCl). Minerals are chemical compounds; for example, the chemical compound NaCl is the mineral halite, also known as table salt. Minerals are not exactly like the chemical compounds you might create in a chemistry lab. To be a mineral, a compound must meet four requirements (p. 94):

(1)   It must be naturally formed. This means that a synthetic ruby is not a mineral, technically.
(2)   It must be a solid. This means that oil, for example, is not a mineral.
(3)   It must have a specific chemical composition. This means that we can express its composition by a chemical formula, like the formula NaCl; however, it doesn't necessarily mean that the chemical composition of the mineral will be simple. An example of a complex chemical formula is that of the mineral amphibole: $Ca_2Mg_5(Si_4O_{11})_2(OH)_2$.
(4)   It must have a characteristic crystal structure. This means that the atoms in the mineral are arranged in an orderly manner, with a symmetrical pattern. So a material such as glass, in which the atoms are arranged in a chaotic manner, cannot be called a mineral.

Minerals are classified according to their chemical and physical properties (pp. 94-102); the most common minerals in the Earth belong to a group called silicates. *[I usually bring with me to class a variety of minerals and mineral-like substances. It helps if you bring along some common substances, like table salt, glass, plastic wrap (a petroleum product, but not a mineral), etc. A large sample of a micaceous mineral such as biotite, with its perfect cleavage, is best for demonstrating how the crystal structures of minerals can influence their physical properties.]*

Rocks are not the same as minerals (p. 103), but most rocks are made of minerals. The three families of rocks are igneous rocks, sedimentary rocks, and metamorphic rocks. They are classified according to their textures and mineral assemblages (pp. 103-105). Internal Earth processes such as volcanism and mountain-building constantly interact with external processes such as the action of wind and water to move rocks around and change them from one form into another. We call this continual circuit of transformations the rock cycle (pp. 105-106).

CHAPTER 5
The Heat Within: Magmas and Volcanoes

SYNOPSIS/LECTURE LEAD-IN

Like earthquakes, volcanoes can cause great human suffering. Many hazards are associated with volcanic eruptions (pp. 123-124), such as pyroclastic flows, poisonous gas emissions, mudflows, and tsunami, as well as secondary hazards like fires, floods, and famine. Some very large eruptions, like the eruption of Krakatau in 1883 (p. 113), can have long-lasting impacts on global climate. This interaction of volcanism with atmospheric processes has been an important feature of the Earth system since the origin of the Earth; indeed, our atmosphere is a secondary one, formed by the degassing of the Earth through volcanism.

Volcanoes have furthered our scientific understanding of the Earth system. The 1883 eruption of Krakatau was significant not only because of its great size *[the explosion was heard by human ears 4600 km away!!]* and its impacts on global climate *[causing anomalous cooling for five years following the eruption]*, but because it was the first major eruption to occur after the establishment of a global network of communications. This meant that scientists across the world knew of the eruption within hours of its occurrence, and were thus able to watch out for global effects. The gas, dust, and ash released by the eruption of Krakatau allowed scientists to learn much about the structure of the atmosphere that had not been previously known.

Volcanoes also bring samples to the surface from deep within the Earth; we do not yet have the technology to drill down into the mantle to bring back samples, so rocks carried up by volcanoes are our only direct link with the materials that make up the Earth's mantle. Volcanoes are beneficial for life on Earth in other ways, too. Through volcanism, the surface of the Earth is replenished. It is no accident that fertile soils often lie downwind of volcanoes. Volcanoes are also instrumental in the geologic formation of some types of ore deposits, and sometimes they can supply power in the form of geothermal energy.

All volcanoes are not alike. The properties of the molten material that erupts from a volcano—called magma while it is under the ground, and lava when it flows out on the surface (pp. 114-115)—have a lot to do with determining both the eruptive style of the volcano and the shape of the volcanic edifice. Some volcanoes, like those in Hawaii, erupt very quietly, with hot, fluid lavas running out over the surface of the land. Others, like Krakatau and Mount St. Helens, erupt with furious explosivity, shooting hot gases and pyroclastic material high into the atmosphere (pp. 116-119). Not all magma makes it to the surface of the Earth. Magma that solidifies underground becomes intrusive igneous rock, while lava that solidifies on the surface becomes extrusive igneous rock (pp. 125-130). The melting of rock and the formation of magmas and igneous rocks can be explained in the context of the plate tectonic cycle (pp. 130-132).

CHAPTER 6
The Principles of Plate Tectonics

SYNOPSIS/LECTURE LEAD-IN

The theory of plate tectonics is a unifying theory or model that geologists use to explain the processes of continental drift, mountain-building, volcanism, the locations of earthquakes, and many other features of the Earth's surface. Observational evidence for plate tectonics had been gathering for many, many years prior to the advent of the theory itself in the mid-1960s. As early as the 1500s, Leonardo da Vinci (1452-1519) recognized that vertical motion (uplift) must have occurred in some continental areas:

> *Sufficient for us is the testimony of things produced in the salt waters and now found again in the high mountains, sometimes far from the sea.*

In the early 1900s, German scientist Alfred Wegener amassed an impressive array of evidence in support of the hypothesis that lateral movements of the continents, as well as vertical uplifts, had occurred (p. 137). Although Wegener's body of evidence was very convincing, most scientists of the time did not accept the hypothesis of continental drift, primarily because they could not imagine a mechanism whereby such motion could be accomplished; the theory of plate tectonics supplied a mechanism.

Three things were instrumental in persuading scientists that continental drift could be explained by the theory of plate tectonics (pp. 140-141):

(1) the hypothesis, first proposed by Harry Hess, that ocean floors were spreading apart along mid-ocean ridges, called seafloor spreading;

(2) strong evidence in support of seafloor spreading, found in the symmetric paleomagnetic striping of volcanic rocks on the seafloor; and

(3) the discovery, through seismic studies, of the aesthenosphere, a layer of relatively weak, mobile material lying just below the cold, brittle lithosphere.

The theory of plate tectonics states that the brittle outermost shell of the Earth (the lithosphere) consists of a number of large segments (plates) that essentially "float" on the weaker lithosphere below (p. 142). Plate motion is almost certainly driven by convective motion of material in the mantle (pp. 153-154), although the exact mechanisms are not clearly understand. When lithospheric plates move around, they interact with one another along divergent (spreading) margins, convergent (collisional or subduction margins), or transform (lateral motion) margins (pp. 147-153). These interactions have fundamentally important consequences for the inhabitants of the Earth's surface, because they shape the Earth's topography and they are a focal point for geologic activity, such as earthquakes and volcanic eruptions.

[The classic demonstration of plate tectonics involves the use of a large, flat pan over a hot plate or heating element. Fill the pan with corn syrup, molasses, or (better yet) wax, and place wooden models of the continents on top of the viscous fluid. Assemble the "continents" together in the center of the pan, in the form of the supercontinent Pangaea. As you heat the fluid to boiling (observing proper safety procedures, of course), the convective action will force the continents apart. If you use wax, it will quickly begin to form a thin crust after you turn off

the heating element, and with some practice you can simulate features like midocean spreading centers in the waxy crust.]

CHAPTER 7
The Earth's Evolving Crust

SYNOPSIS/LECTURE LEAD-IN

Unlike the other planets in our solar system, the Earth has a crust that is constantly changing and evolving. As James Hutton, the originator of the principle of uniformitarianism, stated in 1785:

> *The surface of the land is made by nature to decay...Our fertile plains are formed from the ruins of the mountains.*

We now understand these changes in the context of plate tectonics and the rock cycle, by which mountains are uplifted, only to be worn away by the processes of erosion. Through the continual activity of rock cycle, rocks are broken down into regolith, sediment is transported and deposited, and sedimentary rocks are formed.

When sediment is deposited, sedimentary strata—layers— result (pp. 160-161). Sediments are deposited in strata that are horizontal, or nearly so, and parallel to the Earth's surface. And in any sequence of sedimentary strata the order in which the strata were deposited is from the bottom to the top. These two rules—the law of original horizontality and the principle of stratigraphic superposition—seem almost glaringly obvious to us now, but they were almost revolutionary when first proposed in the middle 1800s. They are the fundamental concepts on which stratigraphy, the study of sedimentary strata, is based. *[You can illustrate original horizontality and superposition using a large graduated cylinder partially filled with water, into which you pour successive batches of sediment of different grain size and/or color, allowing each batch to settle to the bottom.]* Stratigraphy enabled geologists to correlate the relative ages of rocks from one locality to another (pp. 160-162). This, in turn, made possible the establishment of a kind of rock "calendar," of relative ages, which we call the Geologic Column (p. 163). When radioactive age dating was discovered in 1896, geologists were able to calibrate the Geologic Column with absolute ages.

Through the processes of plate tectonics, rocks are subjected to great stress and high temperatures; sometimes they change (metamorphose) into different types of rock in response to these changes in temperature and pressure (pp. 170-178). Metamorphism can result from physical processes such as grinding or crushing, causing mechanical deformation of the rock, or it can involve chemical recrystallization, including changes in the chemical compositions of minerals or the growth of new minerals. Plate tectonics *[as shown in Figure 7.15 in the text]* provides a context and an explanation for the distribution of the different types of metamorphic rocks.

Continental areas are made up of two kinds of structural unit: cratons, which are very old, stable rock platforms; and orogens, which are elongate belts of intensely deformed crust. The presence of orogens—remnants of very ancient continental collisions— sandwiched between ancient cratons provides evidence that the processes of plate tectonics have been operating for a very long time, at least 1.8 billion years.

PART THREE
The Earth's Blanket of Water and Ice

SYNOPSIS/LECTURE LEAD-IN

The presence of water in three forms—liquid, solid, and gas—at the surface of the Earth makes this planet unique. There's really a lot of it, too; more than 70% of the surface is covered by oceans, and a significant amount of the rest is covered by vast ice sheets. As Soviet cosmonaut Oleg Makarov commented:

> *Only from space can you see that our planet should not be called Earth, but rather Water, with specklike islands of dryness on which people, animals, and birds surprisingly find a place to live.*

Water is constantly in a state of movement, continuously cycling from one great reservoir to another. Water in its various forms is responsible for wearing away mountains, shaping the landscape, and transporting and depositing sediment. An important (though volumetrically minor) component of the atmosphere is water, in the form of vapour and fine droplets (i.e., clouds). Of all the cycles that move material from one reservoir to another in the Earth system, the hydrologic cycle is arguably the most important in terms of the maintenance of life on Earth.

CHAPTER 8
The World Ocean

SYNOPSIS/LECTURE LEAD-IN

More than 97 percent of the water in the Earth's hydrosphere is salt water, residing in the oceans. The Pacific Ocean alone is larger in areal extent than all the land masses of the Earth put together. Most of the water on the planet is contained in three huge interconnected basins—the Pacific, Atlantic, and Indian Oceans—all three of which are connected to the Southern Ocean that encircles Antarctica. Together these four vast interconnected water bodies, with innumerable smaller water bodies, make up the world ocean (p. 197).

[It is worth noting that, even though we are land-dwellers, our lives are tied to the ocean in a number of ways. The most obvious is our extensive dependence on the living resources of the ocean, as well as our use of the ocean to support activities ranging from transportation and shipping to tourism and recreation. Oceans also play a critical role in our global climate system, particularly in the stabilization of the atmosphere. Ocean processes and their effects on precipitation and wind systems are largely responsible for determining regional climatic patterns and local weather fluctuations. There is a delicately balanced, dynamic interplay between the oceans and the atmosphere, involving a constant exchange of heat, moisture, and gases. In many respects, the ocean and atmosphere are inextricably linked, complementary parts of one complex, dynamic system. The role of the ocean in regulating climate is discussed in greater detail in Chapter 10.]

The Earth has had liquid water on its surface for at least 3.95 billion years, so the world ocean must have been created sometime between the origin of the Earth (4.6 billion years ago) and 3.95 billion years ago (p. 198). Given the age of the ocean, and the fact that rivers are constantly carrying salts to the ocean from eroded rocks on land, it is surprising that the salinity of seawater has remained constant for many millions (perhaps even billions) of years. The reason is that the processes of extraction or loss of salt from seawater are in a state of balance (steady state) with the processes of addition or influx of salt (p. 199-201).

The chemical and physical properties of ocean water (temperature, salinity, density) vary considerably, with both latitude and depth (pp. 201-202). The circulation of near-surface ocean currents is driven by the interaction of three main elements of the Earth system:

(1)   radiation from the Sun provides heat energy to the atmosphere;
(2)   nonuniform heating generates winds; and
(3)   the winds, in turn, drive the motion of the ocean's surface water (p. 203).

Ocean currents are also influenced by the Coriolis effect (pp. 203-204). *[You can demonstrate the Coriolis effect by using a spinning circular tray, like a large "lazy Susan". Once the tray is spinning, roll a ball from the outer edge towards the center, and watch from above; you will see the ball veer off course because of the Coriolis effect.]* There are also large, deep currents in the ocean, driven by the temperature and salinity characteristics of ocean water. These currents propel the global thermohaline circulation system, through which huge masses of ocean water flow as if on a huge conveyor belt (pp. 210-212).

Waves are surface features of ocean water. They receive their energy from winds that blow across the water surface (pp. 212-216). Breaking waves are important in the formation of coastal landforms.

Tides are caused by the gravitational attraction between the Moon and the Earth (pp. 216-218). The gravitational attraction creates tidal bulges (water level distortions), which remain stationary beneath the tide-producing body (the Moon) while the Earth rotates. This means that twice a day, at every high tide, a mass of water essentially "runs into" the coastline, where it piles up. This water then flows back to the ocean basin as the coastline passes beyond each tidal bulge.

Sea levels fluctuate daily as a result of tides, but longer-term changes in sea level can also be caused by changes in water volume as glaciers wax and wane, or by changes in ocean-basin volume as lithospheric plates shift their positions (pp. 219-220). Around the world there are localities which present geologic evidence that their coastlines have recently emerged (i.e., sea level has dropped relative to the land surface) or submerged (i.e., sea level has risen relative to the land surface, drowning coastal features.

CHAPTER 9
Water on the Land: Surface Streams and Groundwater

SYNOPSIS/LECTURE LEAD-IN

Water on the land is an important part of the Earth system, not only as a crucial freshwater resource for the maintenance of life (less than 3 percent of the water in the hydrosphere is freshwater, and most of it is locked up in ice sheets), but also because of the work of running water in shaping the landscape. This work is in evidence almost everywhere on the land surface of this planet. Even where there are no rivers flowing today, much of the crust is covered by sediment, sedimentary rock, and landforms shaped by running water. This tells us that water in streams and water flowing over the land have been instrumental in shaping our landscape (p. 226). *[If you have access to a good set of planetary slides, you might want to do a brief visual comparison with your students of terrestrial landforms to features thought to have been formed by running water on Mars.]*

When water falls as precipitation, some of it seeps into the ground, through a process known as infiltration, and joins the groundwater. The rest is runoff, flowing towards the oceans either as overland flow or in well-defined stream channels (p. 226-227). Streams have always been central factors in the historical development of settlements and civilizations. The banks of the Nile, for example, have been occupied by people for over seven millenia (p. 225). We rely on streams for freshwater for drinking, washing, irrigation, and industrial use; for their living resources; for transportation; and for recreation. Streams also replenish the land along their banks, by flooding periodically and bringing new, fresh sediment to downstream areas (pp. 231-234). The construction of the Aswan Dam, for example, interfered with flooding and the transport of sediment by the Nile River. This had serious impacts on agricultural soil fertility along the banks of the Nile (p. 225). *[The interference with sediment transport also has caused serious problems along the Mediterranean, where the coast is retreated due to sediment starvation, and fish populations that relied on nutrients brought in by the sediment of the Nile have been dying out.]* Dams are probably the main type of impact of human activity on streams, but other activities—such as mining, logging, industry, and agriculture—may also have negative impacts on the quality and quantity of water flowing in streams.

Less than 1 percent of the water in the hydrosphere is groundwater, defined as all the water contained in spaces within bedrock and regolith. Although the percentage of groundwater seems small, it is 40 times larger than the volume of all the water in freshwater lakes or flowing in streams, and nearly a third as large as the water contained in all the world's glaciers and polar ice (p. 236). Groundwater is thus an integral part of the hydrologic cycle, and a crucial resource for people as well. With respect to the use of groundwater as a resource, there are two central concerns:

(1)   maintaining a balance between the rates of recharge and withdrawal in the aquifer; and
(2)   maintaining the quality of the water in the aquifer.

Groundwater resources can be seriously depleted if water is withdrawn at rates faster than the rate at which the aquifer is naturally recharged (pp. 238-240). When this happens, water tables can fall and sometimes the ground surface even subsides. The chemistry of groundwater is influenced by the rocks and sediment through which it flows (pp. 241-242). Human activities can also influence the chemistry of groundwater. When sewage and other types of waste are disposed of, chemicals are leached from the waste by water that percolates through. This leachate, and the chemicals it carries, will eventually join the groundwater (pp. 243-246).

CHAPTER 10
The World of Snow and Ice

SYNOPSIS/LECTURE LEAD-IN

Of the small proportion of freshwater in the Earth's hydrosphere (less than 3 percent of the total water), the majority of it (87 percent) occurs in the form of snow and ice. The part of the Earth system that remains permanently frozen is called the cryosphere. Glaciers—permanent bodies of ice (p. 254)—are a crucial part of the Earth system, in part because of their role in regulating climate. Glaciers represent a balance between air temperature and precipitation; glacial processes both control and respond to changes in these factors. They can also influence the quantity and characteristics of water in the ocean basins.

Glaciers form wherever snow and ice accumulate from year to year, i.e., where snowfall exceeds snowmelt from one year to the next (p. 257). This means that glaciers don't just form in cold areas like Greenland or Antarctica, but also in temperate regions where high mountains are adjacent to oceans (as a source of moisture for snowfall). Glaciers don't remain the same size from year to year; they grow and shrink along an equilibrium line, in response to the balance between air temperature and precipitation (p. 259). They also don't stay in the same place; glaciers move by internal flow and also by basal sliding (pp. 260-262). *[A time-lapse film showing glacial motion is a good complement to this material. See Audio-Visual references for ideas.]* Sometimes they move and change their shape very quickly, by dramatic processes such as calving or surging (pp. 262-263). *[The Bering Glacier is now in the middle of a major surge. See Suggestions for Further Reading to find out more about it.]*

[You can simulate internal flow in a glacier using Silly Putty® on an inclined surface. Start it flowing, perhaps with a line of toothpicks in it for reference, at the beginning of the lecture, and check it at the end. Try it out first, because the rate of flow will depend on the temperature, degree of incline, and type of Silly Putty®!]

Sea ice (pp. 265-268) and permafrost (pp. 269-271) are also important parts of the cryosphere. Interactions among sea ice, ocean, and atmosphere in the seasonal ice zone influence both the structure and circulation of ocean water. Permafrost—permanently frozen ground—occurs in periglacial regions, which cover more than 25 percent of the Earth's land area.

CHAPTER 11
The Changing Face of the Land

SYNOPSIS/LECTURE LEAD-IN

Internal and external Earth processes meet and interact at the surface of the Earth. That is why the Earth's surface is such a dynamic place to live, and why it is constantly changing and evolving. Weathering and erosion (p. 278) represent the interface between the atmosphere, hydrosphere, and solid Earth. Through physical, mechanical processes (like cracking), and through chemical reactions with the chemicals in water or air (like oxidation or dissolution), rocks and minerals are slowly broken down and transported away (pp. 279-281).

The process of soil formation adds another dimension to this interaction—the biosphere. Soil contains weathered, broken-down regolith and organic material derived from the decay of dead plants and animals (pp. 281-283). This was stated more poetically by Grenville Cole in 1913:

The soil, considered as a rock, links common stones with the atmosphere, and the dead dust of the earth with the continuity of life.

Soil is a critical resource for agriculture, particularly with the human population of the world growing at such a high rate. Soil loss through accelerated erosion is considered by many experts to be the most important limiting factor in determining agricultural productivity and thus food security for the people of the world.

The movement of Earth material doesn't always happen by the slow, inexorable work of weathering and sediment transport. Sometimes huge masses of Earth material break away and move suddenly downslope, under the influence of gravity. We call this mass-wasting, but the result is what is commonly known as a landslide (pp. 284-287).

All of this constant movement of rock and regolith by surface water, groundwater, ice, and wind produces characteristic landforms and terrains (pp. 287-299). What are the landforms that characterize the area where you live and learn? Was the landscape glacially scoured during the last Ice Age (p. 293-295)? Do you live in a semi-arid region, where the work of the wind is in evidence in surrounding landforms (pp. 297-299)? Is your region characterized by huge, interconnected cave systems and sinkhole, the work of groundwater dissolution (pp. 291-293)? Or is running water the main determinant of landscape features in your region (pp. 287-290)? Coastal zones, too, have distinctive landforms, created by the interaction between land and water along the shoreline. If you live in a coastal zone, can you identify the type of coastline and the landforms that characterize it? *[This is a good time to take your students on a field trip, if possible, to look at the landforms around them, or send them out on their own to observe these features. I find that many students, especially non-geology majors, are very unaware of even the most obvious landforms, such as valleys, caves, and raised shorelines. It is worth calling their attention to these features and how they were formed.]*

With weathering and erosion constantly at work, students might wonder why mountains manage to exist at all. But of course, the processes of mountain-building and uplift (through the tectonic cycle) are constantly at work against the processes of weathering and erosion (pp. 305-306). And the changing height and distribution of land masses, in turn, influences climate and precipitation—another example of how the different parts of the Earth system are all interconnected and affect one another.

PART FOUR
The Earth's Gaseous Envelope

SYNOPSIS/LECTURE LEAD-IN

In the origin and evolution of the Earth's atmosphere, we have one of the truly great examples of how different parts of the Earth system are linked together and influence one another. The story of the Earth's atmosphere is a story of gases released through volcanism. These gases contained water vapor, which eventually condensed—when the Earth cooled sufficiently—to form the hydrosphere. Interactions between the land, air, and water throughout Earth history have influenced the chemical composition of the hydrosphere.

But none of these interactions have been as significant as the influence of the biosphere on the chemical evolution of the atmosphere. In the absence of life, there was no free oxygen in the atmosphere. And the biosphere performs a fundamentally important job in acting as a "sink" for carbon dioxide. Without the removal of carbon by organic matter and limestone, the composition of the Earth's atmosphere would be dominated by CO_2, much like the atmosphere of Venus. *[You can return here to the question posed in Part I of the book: Why did the Earth and Venus—alike in so many respects—evolve along such different pathways? The answer lies in the influence of the biosphere on the chemical evolution of the atmosphere.]*

The atmosphere of the Earth is uniquely suited to host life. Without the unique characteristics of our atmosphere, the Earth would be like other planets in the solar system: barren and lifeless. We take for granted the comfortable environment provided for us by the atmosphere, as we take for granted its stability, its resilience, and its apparently limitless extent. Yet, in many respects, nothing could be more fragile than this thin wisp of gases:

> *Photographs from space show the atmosphere in true proportion: a membrane like the skin on an apple. Compared to the solid bulk of the Earth, air is next to nothing. (W. Hively (1989) Tropical forests and Bill Buckner's legs. Amer. Sci., Vol. 77.)*

For all this fragility, the atmosphere provide far more for life on Earth than just the air we breathe: a protective layer of ozone in the atmosphere shields us from harmful ultraviolet radiation (Chapters 12 & 18); oxygen is available in appropriate quantities for respiration, and carbon dioxide and water vapor for photosynthesis (Chapter 15); gases and water vapor trap the Sun's heat near the surface of the Earth, warming it just enough to sustain life (Chapter 14); and interactions among the atmosphere, oceans, and land masses create weather and precipitation patterns (Chapters 12 & 13).

CHAPTER 12
Composition and Structure of the Atmosphere

SYNOPSIS/LECTURE LEAD-IN

[This chapter focuses mainly on the characteristics and structure of the atmosphere. Weather-related processes are discussed in Chapter 13, and the larger-scale processes of the Earth's climate system in Chapter 14.] The atmosphere is very active. It receives its energy from two main sources: the Sun's heat and the Earth's rotation (p. 314). Solar radiation is responsible for the formation of clouds, rain, snow, and much of local weather variation. The Earth's rotation, by contrast, is mainly responsible for large-scale effects in the atmosphere, such as the jet stream and global wind systems.

Because it is well-mixed, the composition of the atmosphere is fairly uniform with respect to its main components. But two important trace components of the atmosphere vary significantly from place to place. They are aerosols and water vapor (p. 315). The atmosphere is dominated by nitrogen, oxygen, and argon, which together make up 99.96 percent of dry air by volume. However, some of the most important characteristics of the atmosphere are related not to these three main gases but to a group of trace gases called the greenhouse gases, which includes carbon dioxide, methane, ozone, nitrous oxide, and water vapor. Together these gases create the Earth's life-maintaining blanket, warming the surface by trapping infrared radiation *[Figure 12.3, the greenhouse effect]*, and protecting the surface and the biosphere from harmful radiation by absorbing ultraviolet rays *[Figure 12.4, the ozone layer]*.

The atmosphere is layered, especially with respect to temperature (p. 320-322). In fact, we define the structure of the atmosphere according to this temperature stratification. The troposphere is the layer nearest the ground, where most of the mass of the atmosphere resides, and where most weather processes originate. The stratosphere, the mesosphere, and the thermosphere are succeeding layers, each with its own temperature characteristics (pp. 317-318).

Much of the atmospheric activity involved in the generation of weather has to do with changes in the state of water in the atmosphere. Of the possible changes *[Figure 12.12]*, the most important are evaporation and condensation, which give rise to clouds, fogs, and rain, and are responsible for the movement of huge amounts of heat from equatorial regions toward the poles (pp. 323-326). Clouds are visible aggregations of minute water droplets, tiny ice crystals, or both. They form when air rises and becomes water-saturated in response to adiabatic cooling (pp. 327-328). There are many different types of clouds; they are classified by their shape, appearance, and height. The three main families of clouds are cumulus, stratus, and cirrus clouds (pp. 327-331).

CHAPTER 13
Winds, Weather, and Desert

SYNOPSIS/LECTURE LEAD-IN

Weather and climate originate in the atmosphere; planets with no atmosphere have no wind and no precipitation, and therefore cannot really be said to have weather. Weather refers to the state of the atmosphere at a given time and place, whereas climate refers to patterns of weather established for a given region over a longer time scale. Weather-forming processes on Earth are driven by energy from the Sun and by the turning of the Earth (particularly the Coriolis effect), and influenced by the distribution and characteristics of land and water masses.

[In reference to chaos theory and its applications to weather prediction, meteorologists sometimes mention the Butterfly Effect. The formation of weather is an example of a process that is sensitive to initial conditions. This means that a very small change at the beginning of the process may have significant consequences for the outcome. In other words, if a butterfly hovering somewhere in Asia flaps its wings an extra beat, the wind it creates may become so

magnified through the complexities of weather formation that it causes a tornado in Iowa!]

Uneven heating of air in the troposphere causes masses of air to rise and fall *[this is discussed in detail in Chapter 12]*, and creates horizontal variations in air pressure. Air flows from regions of high pressure towards regions of low pressure, and this is basically the origin of wind (p. 338). *[If you are willing to go to a bit of trouble, you can create a wind tunnel for the study of wind and aeolian landforms. Use a long box, such as a box for a refrigerator, and set up a fan at one end. You will need a screen to diffuse the wind. Get some sand, and experiment with dune formation and the landforms created by sand blowing around different-shaped obstacles.]*

Once wind exists, a variety of factors affect its speed and direction, including the air pressure gradient, the Coriolis effect, and friction. These factors combine to create forms of flow in winds that are similar to the types of flow observed in ocean currents *[Chapter 8]*. For example, when air near the ground flows toward a low-pressure center, an inward spiral motion develops. This is essentially the same as the spiralling currents, called Ekman spirals, observed in ocean water and described in Chapter 8 (pp. 340-342). Inward-spiralling air currents around a low-pressure center are called cyclones, while outward-spiralling currents around a high-pressure zone are called anticyclones (p. 342). Sometimes moving air masses can develop into truly violent storms, such as tornadoes or hurricanes, which can cause extensive damage.

Solar heat imbalances and the resulting flow of air, combined with Coriolis deflection, create hug global air circulation cells. These cells are responsible for many of the persistent weather features we associate with different parts of the world, such as the tradewinds in the equatorial regions, and westerly winds in the middle latitudes (pp. 343-347). These persistent patterns of air circulation determine, to a great extent, the distribution of global belts of high rainfall and low rainfall (pp. 347-348). In some areas, local wind systems created by the interaction of wind with specific types of terrain or topography can be even more important than global air circulation patterns in determining the weather (pp. 351-352.

CHAPTER 14
The Earth's Climate System

SYNOPSIS/LECTURE LEAD-IN

Everyone seems to be concerned about global climate these days. There are lots of questions, and no one seems to have answers for all of them. Is the Earth's climate warming? How can we tell? What factors control global climate? What will happen if the climate does get warmer? Will the ice caps melt? Will sea level increase? There are lots of questions, but few definite answers. Part of the reason is that the factors that control global climate are indeed very complex. Climate is regulated by a network of intricately interrelated processes involving all parts of the Earth system as well as astronomical characteristics (p. 381-382); these processes and interactions are only partially understood. The subsystems of the Earth's climate system *[Figure 14.1]*—atmosphere, ocean, cryosphere, lithosphere, and biosphere—interact so closely that a change in one of these subsystems can lead to changes in one or more of the others (p. 362).

Another reason for so many unanswered questions is that human activity is now known to cause changes in the atmosphere. These changes may have long-term consequences for global climate. The changes caused by human actions; their impacts on global climate; and the social, political, economic, and technological factors that influence these changes are all poorly understood, and this leads to a lot of unanswered questions. Human influences on global climate are covered in detail in Chapter 18. In Chapter 14, the authors focus on the physical processes that control and regulate climate, and on how scientists study and monitor climatic changes.

One of the most important aspects of the study of climate is to unravel the history of climatic changes, and to try to discover the factors that controlled or initiated climatic changes at other times in Earth history. *[If you live in a part of the world that was ice-covered during the last glaciation, students generally find it interesting to learn that the place where they now sit was once covered by 1 or 2 kilometers of ice!]* Because we can't go back in time hundreds of thousands of years to observe or measure these changes directly, we must use substitutes—proxies—to draw information about past climatic change from the geologic record. A climate proxy record is a record of changes in an Earth process that closely mimics and is controlled by climate (p. 366). Scientists use a wide variety of ingenious methods to study past climatic changes. Many of these studies have helped us toward a better understanding of the possible impacts of human action on global climate.

PART FIVE
The Dynamics of Life on Earth

SYNOPSIS/LECTURE LEAD-IN

By now it will be clear to students of this course exactly how unique is the role played by the biosphere in the Earth system. Life on Earth is totally dependent on the special characteristics of the Earth's atmosphere, hydrosphere, solid Earth, and even its relationship with the Sun. But throughout the evolution of this planet the biosphere, in turn, has had a significant influence on the atmosphere, the hydrosphere, and even the regolith. This influence continues today.

Here, as in the study of other parts of the Earth system, we may have more questions than answers at this point. Many of the most pressing questions stem from the issues surrounding the preservation of biological diversity on Earth. How have the millions of types of living creatures alive today evolved into their current states? Exactly how many species are there on Earth today?

Why have some species died out in the geologic past, while others have endured for millions of years? Why is it important to maintain biological diversity? When changes occur in other parts of the Earth system (the atmosphere, hydrosphere, or solid Earth), what are the implications for biological diversity?

In this part of the book, Chapter 15 focuses on the functioning of the global ecosystem, the types of organisms alive today, and how they live and interact with one another, with different Earth subsystems, and with humans. In Chapter 16, the authors address yet another of the great stories of interaction and interconnection in the Earth system: the story of the origin and evolution of life on Earth.

CHAPTER 15
Dynamics of the Global Ecosystem

SYNOPSIS/LECTURE LEAD-IN

E.O. Wilson, a well-known biologist, once wrote:

The diversity of life forms, so numerous that we have yet to identify most of them, is the greatest wonder of this planet. (Biodiversity, 1991, E.O. Wilson, ed., Nat'l. Acad. Sci.).

We really don't even know how many species are alive today; some 1.4 million species have been described, but scientists estimate the absolute number of species on the planet to be somewhere between 5 and 30 million!

If so many types of organisms are alive, then why are we worried about preserving biological diversity? We can begin to answer that very difficult question by looking at the situation in the tropical rainforests, the most biologically diverse habitat on Earth. The cutting down of tropical rainforests is thought by biologists to be responsible for a rate of extinction of about 10,000 species per year (compared to the natural rate of extinction of about 8 species per year). This means that the current extinction rate, created by human actions, rivals the greatest mass extinctions we know of in the long history of life on Earth, the catastrophic extinctions that occurred at the ends of the Paleozoic and Mesozoic eras—in other words, we are currently witnessing (or causing, to be more precise) the greatest mass extinction to have occurred at any time in the past 65 million years.

The web-like relationships through which a population of organisms transfer energy (in the form of food), together with the habitat that supports the population, is called an ecosystem (pp. 392-393). Ecosystems are easily disturbed, but they are also resilient. Populations in an ecosystem are regulated by internal factors, such as competition for niches, and they also respond to external factors such as climatic change and catastrophic events like volcanic eruptions (pp. 394-395).

The diversity of an ecosystem, i.e., the number of species that inhabits it, is influenced by a variety of factors, including climate, sexual reproduction, evolutionary innovations, provinciality, and niche availability (pp. 396-402). Diversity in the global ecosystem is influenced by all of these factors, which in turn are affected by plate tectonics through the redistribution of land masses (p. 403-404). As mentioned above, human action is now rivalling all natural causes as a controlling factor on biological diversity in the global ecosystem.

CHAPTER 16
Evolution of the Biosphere

SYNOPSIS/LECTURE LEAD-IN

This chapter addresses three unanswered questions. How did the biosphere begin or, how did life start on the Earth? Along what pathways and by what mechanisms did life evolve from its microscopic beginnings to the complex biosphere that exists today? And what have been the effects of the changing and evolving biosphere on the Earth system over geologic time?

No one knows how life began or what the first cell was like, but it must have been an anaerobic procaryote (a simple cell, not dependent on oxygen for respiration). The exact mechanism whereby life originated is unclear, but we know that it must have involved chemosynthesis, i.e., the synthesis of small organic molecules like amino acids (pp. 419-420), and biosynthesis, the polymerization of small organic molecules to form biopolymers. The final step was the development of the complex machinery of DNA and RNA, needed for the replication of living organisms.

[One of the most interesting things about the whole debate concerning the origins of life on Earth is the number of different environments that have been proposed. You would think that the type of environment suitable for life to originate would have to be a very singular environment, indeed, but this is apparently not the case. Environments that have been suggested to have appropriate characteristics for the development of early life forms include hydrothermal seafloor vents ("black smokers"); thermal hot springs and geysers; warm pools of surface water, such as tidal pools (the "soup" of the Oparin hypothesis); and even sea foam. And of course the hypothesis that the organic precursors for life were originally delivered to the Earth via comets remains a viable one, supported by the discovery of protein-like molecules in some meteorites.]

We study the history of life on Earth by looking at the remnants of life forms preserved in the rock record—i.e., by studying fossils. Fossil procaryotes have been found in rocks as old as 3.5 billion years, so we can deduce that life must have originated quite early in Earth history (pp. 418-419). Eucaryotes appeared about 1.4 billion years ago; the first to appear were single-celled green algae (pp. 425-426). This means that billions of years of the history of life on Earth were dominated by single-celled organisms. The earliest fossils of multicellular organisms appear in rocks about 600 million years old, right about the same time geochemists calculate that oxygen had built up to a sufficient level in the atmosphere for the ozone layer to begin blocking ultraviolet radiation. The subsequent history of life is the history of great explosions in the number and types of species, and evolutionary innovations.

PART SIX
Living on the Earth

SYNOPSIS/LECTURE LEAD-IN

When we consider the Earth as a system, we are faced with accepting some of the fundamental characteristics of that system, such as the fact that its subsystems are interrelated; that the amount of material it contains is finite; and that changes in one part of the system will have an impact elsewhere in the system. These are facts of life on the Earth today, and they have significant implications for the human population of the planet. For one thing, the solid Earth resources of this planet (including water and soil) are limited and finite. We may develop ever more sophisticated techniques for locating and extracting oil or mineral deposits, but in the long run these are exhaustible resources. For another, we must face the fact that the waste-absorbing capacities of the Earth system are also finite; the wastes we put into one part of the system are more likely than ever to have negative impacts somewhere else. Because the human population of the world is approaching the carrying capacity of the planet these limitations seem more real to us than ever before.

As part of the integrated study of the Earth system, we are beginning to recognize the role of human beings in this system, both in terms of our dependence on the workings and resources of the natural system and in terms of our impacts on the system. In this final part of the book, the authors consider these two fundamental realizations. Chapter 17 explores the range of resources we draw from the Earth, upon which we depend for the maintenance of life and civilization. And Chapter 18 addresses the issue of human activity as an agent of global geologic change.

CHAPTER 17
Resources from the Earth

SYNOPSIS/LECTURE LEAD-IN

As we sit in comfort in a heated (or air-conditioned) classroom, it is hard to grasp the depth of our dependence on the resources of the Earth (p. 446). When we talk about Earth resources, typically we include minerals, rocks, and metals extracted from the Earth, and energy resources such as coal or oil. Water, especially groundwater, is usually included, as is soil. The one thing that all of these resources have in common is that they are essentially nonrenewable on the time scale of a human lifetime; this is (or should be) a critical factor in the use and management of these resources. *[With younger children, I sometimes begin a lecture of this type by challenging them to leave the room without making use of Earth resources. Some of them would have to remove their glasses and the braces on their teeth. Most would have to take off their clothes which, except for wool sweaters and cotton t-shirts, have a tendency to be made of synthetic petroleum products or involve chemical dyes or metal rivets. And they would probably have to float out of the room to avoid contact with floor tiles or metal chairs, desks, and doorways. With older students and adults, it may be revealing to point out to them that everything in their car (with the possible exception of leather upholstery) is an Earth resource of one type or another, including the metal, the plastic and synthetic fabrics, the gasoline, and even the "rubber" from the tires, which are now made from oil rather than from rubber.]*

Mineral deposits are formed by a wide variety of geologic processes (influenced, in some cases, by processes in the atmosphere, hydrosphere, and biosphere; pp. 448-456). What we look for, in particular, are processes that concentrate a particular element or material over and above its natural average concentration in the crust of the Earth. When this type of localized concentration occurs, the material may be economically extractable and we call it an ore (p. 447). It is interesting that the processes leading to ore formation, and consequently the locations of major ore deposits (the metallogenic provinces) can be explained quite nicely in the context of a plate tectonic model (pp. 456-457).

The main energy source of modern civilization—fossil fuels—is another type of nonrenewable Earth resource. Fossil fuels really represent solar energy—a very small proportion of the solar energy that reached the Earth's surface millions of years ago, was converted into organic matter by plants and animals, and was preserved in the rock record when those organisms died under very specific geologic conditions (pp. 458-460). Because fossil fuels will be used up one day, and because (in the meantime) we are discovering that their use has negative impacts on the environment, especially the atmosphere, it may be wise to begin turning our attention to other sources of energy. Some possibilities include unconventional fossil fuels, such as oil shales and tar sands; nuclear energy; geothermal energy; solar energy; wind energy; and ocean energy in the form of wind, waves, or tides (pp. 461-465). Each of these alternative energy sources has its own limitations, its own possibilities, and its own environmental implications.

CHAPTER 18
Global Change: A Planet Under Stress

SYNOPSIS/LECTURE LEAD-IN

To a certain extent, global change has been a theme throughout much of the book. We have looked at how the different subsystems of the Earth system interact and influence one another, and at how they work in concert to produce the intricately balanced complexities that characterize this system today. We have also looked at the impacts of human action on the workings of these subsystems, and we have learned that these impacts on the Earth system are being detected on a broader scale than ever before. Some of these impacts are local or regional in extent, encompassing processes such as pollution and eutrophication of surface waters; deforestation and accelerated soil erosion; and desertification due to land degradation (pp. 473-477).

But today when we use the term global change, we are mainly referring to two very specific processes, both of which involve changes to the world's atmosphere imposed by human actions. They are the process of depletion of stratospheric ozone; and the process of enhanced greenhouse warming due to anthropogenic changes in the chemistry of the atmosphere. *[I find that the stories of how scientists first discovered these two problems is of great interest to students, and highlights the human side of Earth science. These stories are related briefly in the text, and in more detail in some of the suggested readings.]*

Without the greenhouse effect, the surface of the Earth would be cold and inhospitable. What we are concerned about is not the natural greenhouse warming, which is effected primarily by water vapor in the atmosphere, but the additions to the atmosphere of large quantities of the so-called greenhouse gases (carbon dioxide, methane, nitrous oxide, and CFCs). The enhanced greenhouse effect caused by anthropogenic emissions of these gases may lead to a substantial warming of the global climate over the next few decades, with far-reaching consequences for all ecosystems, including humans (pp. 477-487). The depletion of stratospheric ozone (pp. 471-472), thought to be caused primarily by a group of industrial chemicals called CFCs, represents a further threat to the health and viability of the biosphere.

The Earth System Sciences Committee of NASA—a group responsible in no small way for the recent surge of interest in the systems approach to Earth science—suggested in their 1986 report that a fundamental part of recognizing the role of humanity in contributing to global change should be to accept responsibility for these changes and for the appropriate stewardship of this planetary system:

> *We, the peoples of the world, face a new responsibility for our global future. Through our economic and technological activity, we are now contributing to significant global changes on the Earth within the span of a few human generations. We have become part of the Earth System and one of the forces for Earth change. (NASA Advisory Council, Earth System Sciences Committee, May 1986).*

SAMPLE COURSE SYLLABI

COURSE OPTIONS

Presented below are three sample course syllabi for courses based on *The Blue Planet:*

1. Syllabus Number 1 is designed for a standard 14-week term, with three one-hour lectures per week, following the format of the book in terms of the order in which topics are presented.

2. Syllabus Number 2 is designed for a full-year course consisting of two 14-week terms with 42 lecture hours in each term. In this syllabus I have assumed that there would be time for lab or classroom demonstrations, approximately one every two weeks, even if the course has no formal lab component. Most of the recommended lab exercises and demonstrations can be found in the *Laboratory Manual for The Blue Planet,* by Marcia Bjørnerud, John M. Hughes and A. Dwight Baldwin, one of the supplements to the text.

3. Syllabus Number 3 is designed for a 14-week term with two one-hour lectures per week; this might be a typical format, for example, in a course with a lab component, or in an "interest" course for non-majors.

ORGANIZATION

The chapters and parts in *The Blue Planet* have been written so that some reorganization of topics is possible without loss of continuity. For example, the chapters on the solar system could be assigned toward the end of the course, rather than at the beginning, and the chapters on the biosphere could be shifted or omitted.

I find it useful to organize my course syllabus into a table, as shown below. You can include a separate column giving the date of each session, as well as important dates for students to remember, such as dates of field trips or due dates for assignments, lab reports, or term papers. When the course is organized in this way, both you and your students can keep track of progress and keep the course on schedule. It makes it a lot easier to fit all the topics into the allocated time. Students also have access to all the information they require, on a single handout.

In each syllabus I have suggested a wide variety of audio-visual resources to complement specific topics. Many other good titles are available; addresses for distributors of these and other resources are provided in the section on Audio-Visual Resources. There is flexibility in each syllabus to add more videos or slides, substitute other titles, or delete some audio-visuals to make room for more detailed lectures.

Earth System Science: Sample Course Syllabus

Number 1: 14-Week Term with 42 Lectures (3 lectures per week)

Week	Lecture Topics	Assigned Reading
1	1. Introduction & Announcements 2. What is Earth System Science? 3. Uniformitarianism & Catastrophism Video: *Down to Earth* (30 minutes; Annenberg/CPB)	Skinner & Porter: Introduction
2	4. Our Place in the Solar System Video: *The Restless Planet* (30 minutes; Annenberg/CPB) 5. The Sun 6. The Earth's Interior	Skinner & Porter: Chapters 1 & 2
3	7. Earthquakes 8. Earthquake Hazards & Prediction 9. Video: *Earthquakes: Prediction and Monitoring* (26 minutes; Films for the Humanities & Sciences)	Skinner & Porter: Chapter 3
4	10. Introduction to Earth Materials 11. Classroom Demonstration and Slides: *Rocks & Minerals* (MMI Corporation or Ward's) 12. Magma, Lava & Igneous Rocks	Skinner & Porter: Chapters 4 & 5
5	13. Volcanic Eruptions 14. Video: *In the Path of a Killer Volcano* (60 minutes; Films for the Humanities & Sciences) 15. Plate Tectonics & Continental Drift	Skinner & Porter: Chapters 5 & 6
6	16. Plate Tectonics & the External Structure of the Earth Video: *The Birth of a Theory* (30 minutes; Annenberg/CPB) ----Cut-off Point for Midterm Test---- 17. Sedimentation & Sedimentary Rocks 18. The Rock Record & Geologic Time Video: *The Record of the Rocks* (20 minutes; Films for the Humanities & Sciences)	Skinner & Porter: Chapters 6 & 7

7	19. 20. 21.	Metamorphism & Metamorphic Rocks Review Session & Question Period for Midterm Test Midterm Test	Skinner & Porter: Chapter 7
8	22. 23. 24.	The Ocean Video: *The Return of the Child: The Effects of El Niño* (26 minutes; Films for the Humanities & Sciences) Surface Water Processes Video: *River Channel Forms* (20 minutes; Films for the Humanities & Sciences) Discussion of Test Results	Skinner & Porter: Chapters 8 & 9
9	25. 26. 27.	Groundwater Processes Human Impacts on Surface Water & Groundwater Glaciers & Sea Ice Video: *Valley Glaciers* (20 minutes; Films for the Humanities & Sciences)	Skinner & Porter: Chapters 9 & 10
10	28. 29. 30.	Weathering, Erosion & Landforms Mass-Wasting Video: *Mass-Wasting* (30 minutes; Annenberg/CPB) The Atmosphere Slides: *The Earth's Atmosphere* (MMI Corporation)	Skinner & Porter: Chapters 11 & 12
11	31. 32. 33.	Wind & Weather Precipitation & Deserts The Earth's Climate System Video: *Modifying the Weather: Case of the Man-Made Desert* (26 minutes; Films for the Humanities & Sciences)	Skinner & Porter: Chapters 13 & 14
12	34. 35. 36.	The Biosphere Human Impacts on the Biosphere Video: *Preserving the Rain Forest* (24 minutes; Films for the Humanities & Sciences) The Origin & Evolution of Life	Skinner & Porter: Chapters 15 & 16
13	37. 38. 39.	Mineral Resources Energy Resources Video: *Gifts from the Earth* (60 minutes; Annenberg/CPB)	Skinner & Porter: Chapter 17

Sample Course Syllabus Number 1, continued			
14	40.	Global Change Video: *Alterations in the Atmosphere* (18 minutes; Films for the Humanities & Sciences)	Skinner & Porter: Chapter 18
	41.	Summary and Conclusions Slides: *Shuttle Views the Earth* (MMI Corporation)	
	42.	Review Session and Question Period for Final Exam	

Earth System Science: Sample Course Syllabus

Number 2: Two 14-Week Terms with 84 Lectures Total (3 lectures per week ± lab)

Week	Lecture Topics		Assigned Reading
1	1. 2. 3.	Introduction & Announcements What is Earth System Science? Uniformitarianism & Catastrophism Video: *Down to Earth* (30 minutes; Annenberg/CPB)	Skinner & Porter: Introduction
2	4. 5. 6.	Basic Laws of Astronomy Our Place in the Solar System Video: *The Restless Planet* (30 minutes; Annenberg/CPB) Lab or Classroom Demonstration: *The Earth in Space* (from *Laboratory Manual*)	Skinner & Porter: Chapter 1
3	7. 8. 9.	Other Planets of the Sun Slides: *The Planetary System* (MMI Corporation) Video: *Tales from Other Worlds* (60 minutes; Annenberg/CPB) The Sun & Stellar Processes Slides: *The Sun* (MMI Corporation)	Skinner & Porter: Chapter 2

4	10.	The Interior of the Earth Video: *Earth's Interior* (30 minutes; Annenberg/CPB)	Skinner & Porter: Chapter 3
	11.	Earthquakes	
	12.	Earthquake Hazards & Prediction Video: *Earthquakes: Prediction and Monitoring* (26 minutes; Films for the Humanities & Sciences) ----Cut-off Point for Term Test #1----	
5	13.	Introduction to Earth Materials Video: *Minerals: The Materials of Earth* (30 minutes; Annenberg/CPB)	Skinner & Porter: Chapter 4
	14.	Classification & Properties of Minerals	
	15.	Classification & Properties of Rocks	
6	16.	Lab or Classroom Demonstration: Rocks & Minerals Slides: *Rocks & Minerals* (MMI Corporation or Ward's)	Skinner & Porter: Chapter 4
	17.	Minerals in Our Environment: Focus on Asbestos	
	18.	Review Session & Question Period for Term Test #1	
7	19.	Term Test #1	Skinner & Porter: Chapter 5
	20.	Video: *In the Path of a Killer Volcano* (60 minutes; Films for the Humanities & Sciences)	
	21.	Volcanoes, Volcanic Materials & Igneous Rocks	
8	22.	Volcanic Hazards	Skinner & Porter: Chapter 5
	23.	Volcanism & Climatic Change	
	24.	Discussion of Term Test #1 Results	
9	25.	Plate Tectonics & Continental Drift Video: *The Birth of a Theory* (30 minutes; Annenberg/CPB)	Skinner & Porter: Chapter 6
	26.	Plate Tectonics & the External Structure of the Earth Slides: *Shuttle Views the Earth: Geology from Space* (MMI Corporation)	
	27.	Lab or Classroom Demonstration: *The Earth Beneath Our Feet* (from *Laboratory Manual*)	

10	28.	Sedimentation & Sedimentary Rocks	Skinner & Porter: Chapter 7
	29.	Rock Strata & Principles of Stratigraphy	
	30.	The Rock Record & Geologic Time	
		Video: *The Record of the Rocks* (20 minutes; Films for the Humanities & Sciences)	
11	31.	Metamorphism & Metamorphic Rocks	Skinner & Porter: Chapter 7
		Video: *Metamorphism* (30 minutes; Annenberg/CPB)	
	32.	Mountain Building & the Structures of Continents	
	33.	Lab or Classroom Demonstration: *The Earth in Time* (from *Laboratory Manual*)	
		----Cut-off Point for Term Test #2----	
12	34.	Ocean Circulation	Skinner & Porter: Chapter 8
	35.	Ocean Waves & Tides	
		Slides: *Oceans & Shorelines* (MMI Corporation)	
	36.	El Niño/Southern Oscillation	
13	37.	Streams & Drainage Systems	Skinner & Porter: Chapter 9
		Video: *Catchment Studies* (20 minutes; Films for the Humanities & Sciences)	
	38.	Lab or Classroom Demonstration: *Earth's Surface in Flux* (from *Laboratory Manual*)	
	39.	Review Session & Question Period for Term Test #2	
14	40.	Term Test #2	Skinner & Porter: Chapter 9
	41.	Groundwater Processes	
	42.	Human Impacts on Surface Water & Groundwater	
		Video: *The Ocean Planet: The Death of the Mississippi* (23 minutes; Films for the Humanities & Sciences)	
15	43.	Glaciers & Sea Ice	Skinner & Porter: Chapter 10
		Video: *Living Glaciers* (30 minutes; Films for the Humanities & Sciences)	
	44.	Glacial Landforms	
		Video: *Glacial Deposits* (20 minutes; Films for the Humanities & Sciences)	
	45.	Discussion of Term Test #2 Results	

16	46.	Weathering Video: *Soils: Profiles & Processes* (20 minutes; Films for the Humanities & Sciences)	Skinner & Porter: Chapter 11
	47.	Erosion & Landforms Slides: *Weathering & Landforms* (MMI Corporation)	
	48.	Mass-Wasting	
17	49.	Composition, Structure & Evolution of the Atmosphere Slides: *The Earth's Atmosphere* (MMI Corporation)	Skinner & Porter: Chapter 12
	50.	Cloud Formation Slides: *Shuttle Views the Earth: Clouds from Space* (MMI Corporation)	
	51.	Lab or Classroom Demonstration: *Earth's Aura: The Atmosphere & Hydrosphere* (from *Laboratory Manual*) ----Cut-off Point for Term Test #3----	
18	52.	Atmospheres on Other Planets: A Comparative Look	Skinner & Porter: Chapter 13
	53.	Wind & Weather Video: *Mapping the Weather* (26 minutes; Films for the Humanities & Sciences)	
	54.	Precipitation & Deserts Video: *Wind, Dust & Deserts* (30 minutes; Annenberg/CPB)	
19	55.	The Earth's Climate System	Skinner & Porter: Chapter 14
	56.	Video: *The Climate Puzzle* (60 minutes; Annenberg/CPB)	
	57.	Review Session & Question Period for Term Test #3	
20	58.	Term Test #3	Skinner & Porter: Chapter 14
	59.	The Geologic Record of Climatic Change	
	60.	Glaciation & Interglaciation	
21	61.	The Biosphere	Skinner & Porter: Chapter 15
	62.	Fundamental Biological & Ecological Processes Video: *The Genetic Code* (30 minutes; Annenberg/CPB)	
	63.	Discussion of Term Test #3 Results	

22	64. 65. 66.	Biodiversity Human Impacts on the Biosphere Lab or Classroom Demonstration: *The Organic Earth* (from *Laboratory Manual*)	Skinner & Porter: Chapter 15
23	67. 68. 69.	Biogeochemical Cycles The Origin of Life Fossils & Fossilization Slides: *The Study of Fossils* (MMI Corporation)	Skinner & Porter: Chapter 16
24	70. 71. 72.	The Evolution of Life I The Evolution of Life II Video: *Evolution Through Time* (30 minutes; Annenberg/CPB) Video: *Remnants of Eden* (60 minutes; Annenberg/CPB)	Skinner & Porter: Chapter 16
25	73. 74. 75.	Mineral Resources Ore-Forming Processes Lab or Classroom Demonstration: *Earth Resources* (from *Laboratory Manual*)	Skinner & Porter: Chapter 17
26	76. 77. 78.	Fossil Fuels Alternative Energy Resources Video: *Gifts from the Earth* (60 minutes; Annenberg/CPB)	Skinner & Porter: Chapter 17
27	79. 80. 81.	Global Change I: Global Warming Global Change II: Ozone Depletion Lab or Classroom Demonstration: *The Imperiled Earth* (from *Laboratory Manual*)	Skinner & Porter: Chapter 18
28	82. 83. 84.	Video: *Only One Atmosphere* (60 minutes; Annenberg/CPB) Summary and Conclusions Slides: *Shuttle Views the Earth* (MMI Corporation) Review Session and Question Period for Final Exam	Skinner & Porter: Chapter 18

Earth System Science: Sample Course Syllabus

Number 3: 14-Week Term with 28 Lectures (2 lectures per week ± lab)

Week	Lecture Topics	Assigned Reading
1	1. Introduction: What is Earth System Science? 2. Our Place in the Solar System Video: *The Restless Planet* (30 minutes; Annenberg/CPB)	Skinner & Porter: Introduction & Chapter 1
2	3. The Sun & Stellar Processes 4. The Earth's Interior	Skinner & Porter: Chapters 2 & 3
3	5. Earthquake Hazards & Prediction Video: *Earthquakes: Prediction and Monitoring* (26 minutes; Films for the Humanities & Sciences) 6. Introduction to Earth Materials	Skinner & Porter: Chapter 3 & 4
4	7. Classroom Demonstration and Slides: *Rocks & Minerals* (MMI Corporation or Ward's) 8. Volcanic Eruptions Slides: *Mount Pinatubo: The 1991 Eruption* (National Oceanic & Atmospheric Administration)	Skinner & Porter: Chapters 4 & 5
5	9. Plate Tectonics & Continental Drift 10. Plate Tectonics & the External Structure of the Earth Video: *The Birth of a Theory* (30 minutes; Annenberg/CPB)	Skinner & Porter: Chapter 6
6	----Cut-off Point for Midterm Test---- 11. Sedimentation & Sedimentary Rocks 12. The Rock Record & Geologic Time Video: *The Record of the Rocks* (20 minutes; Films for the Humanities & Sciences)	Skinner & Porter: Chapters 6 & 7
7	13. Metamorphism & Metamorphic Rocks 14. Midterm Test	Skinner & Porter: Chapters 7 & 8

8	15.	The Ocean Video: *The Return of the Child: The Effects of El Niño* (26 minutes; Films for the Humanities & Sciences)		Skinner & Porter: Chapters 8 & 9
	16.	Surface Water Processes Video: *River Channel Forms* (20 minutes; Films for the Humanities & Sciences)		
9	17.	Groundwater Processes		Skinner & Porter: Chapters 9 & 10
	18.	Glaciers & Sea Ice Video: *Valley Glaciers* (20 minutes; Films for the Humanities & Sciences)		
10	19.	Weathering, Erosion & Mass-Wasting Video: *Mass-Wasting* (30 minutes; Annenberg/CPB)		Skinner & Porter: Chapters 11 & 12
	20.	The Atmosphere Slides: *The Earth's Atmosphere* (MMI Corporation)		
11	21.	Wind & Weather		Skinner & Porter: Chapters 13 & 14
	22.	The Earth's Climate System Video: *Modifying the Weather: The Case of the Man-Made Desert* (26 minutes; Films for the Humanities & Sciences)		
12	23.	The Origin & Evolution of Life		Skinner & Porter: Chapters 15 & 16
	24.	Human Impacts on the Biosphere Video: *Preserving the Rain Forest* (24 minutes; Films for the Humanities & Sciences)		
13	25.	Mineral Resources		Skinner & Porter: Chapter 17
	26.	Energy Resources		
14	27.	Global Change Video: *Alterations in the Atmosphere* (18 minutes; Films for the Humanities & Sciences)		Skinner & Porter: Chapter 18
	28.	Summary and Conclusions Slides: *Shuttle Views the Earth* (MMI Corporation)		

SUGGESTIONS FOR FURTHER READING

These readings may help you to gain a deeper understanding of some of the topics covered in the book. Many of the readings would be appropriate for students' further reading and research, but some of them might be too advanced for undergraduates.

The readings are grouped according to their general subject contents into seven main categories, corresponding to the major divisions in the text (with an additional category for General Earth System Science references). The categories are identified by icons similar to those used as identifiers in the text. For each category, the readings are also grouped into books and reports, and articles.

 THE EARTH IN SPACE

Books & Reports:

Broecker, Wallace S. (1985) *How to Build a Habitable Planet.* Lamont-Doherty Geological Observatory of Columbia University. Eldigio Press, LDGO Box #2, Palisades, NY 10964.

Greely, Ronald (1994) *Planetary Surfaces.* New York: Chapman & Hall.

Kahn, Ralph (1989) *Comparative Planetology and the Atmosphere of the Earth.* A Report of the Solar System Exploration Division. Washington, DC: NASA.

Pecker, J.-C., and Runcorn, S.K., eds. (1990) *The Earth's Climate and Variability of the Sun Over Recent Millenia.* London: The Royal Society.

Stevens, Payson R., and Kelley, Kevin W. (1992) *Embracing Earth: New Views of our Changing Planet.* San Francisco: Chronicle Books.

Zeilik, Michael (1994) *Conceptual Astronomy.* New York: John Wiley & Sons.

Zeilik, Michael (1994) *The Evolving Universe.* New York: John Wiley & Sons, 7th ed.

Articles:

Ahrens, Thomas J. (1994) The origin of the Earth. *Physics Today* (August), pp. 38-45.

Burt, Donald M. (1989) Mining the Moon. *American Scientist,* Vol. 77 (Nov-Dec), pp. 574-579.

Drake, Michael J., Boynton, William V., and Blanchard, Douglas P. (1987) The case for planetary sample return missions: 1. Origin of the solar system. *EOS,* Vol. 68, No. 8 (February 24), pp. 105, 111-113.

Gooding, James L., Carr, Michael H., and McKay, Christopher P. (1989) The case for planetary sample return missions: 2. History of Mars. *EOS,* Vol. 70, No. 31 (August 1), pp. 745, 754-755.

Gribben, John (1993) Inside the Sun. *NewScientist* (March 13), p. 1.

Head, James W., and Solomon, Sean C. (1981) Tectonic evolution of the terrestrial planets. *Science,* Vol. 213 (July 3), pp. 62-76.

Head, James W. III, and Crumpler, L.S. (1987) Evidence for divergent plate-boundary characteristics and crustal spreading on Venus. *Science,* Vol. 238 (December 4), pp. 1380-1385.

Kieffer, Susan W., and Morrissey, Meghan M. (1993) Exploring Earth with new data and tools. *Geotimes* (June), pp. 15-17.

Lean, Judith, and Rind, David (1994) The Sun's effect on global warming. *Earth in Space,* Vol. 6, No. 5 (January), pp. 11-12.

Marvin, Ursula (1990) Bolide impact and its consequences for geology. *Geotimes* (August), pp. 14-15.

Marvin, Ursula (1986) Meteorites, the Moon, and the history of geology. *Journal of Geological Education,* Vol. 34, pp. 140-157.

McSween, Harry Y. Jr. (1989) Chondritic meteorites and the formation of planets. *American Scientist,* Vol. 77 (March-April), pp. 146-153.

Miner, Ellis D. (1990) Voyager 2's encounter with the gas giants. *Physics Today,* Vol. 43, No. 7 (July), pp. 40-47.

Newcott, William (1993) Venus revealed. *National Geographic,* Vol. 183, No. 2, pp. 36-59.

Ryder, Graham, Spudis, Paul D., and Taylor, G. Jeffrey (1989) The case for planetary sample return missions: 3. Origin and evolution of the Moon and its environment. *EOS,* Vol. 70, No. 47 (November 21), pp. 1495, 1505-1509.

Sargent, Anneila I., and Beckwith, Steven V.W. (1993) The search for forming planetary systems. *Physics Today* (April), pp. 22-29.

Saunders, R. Stephen (1990) The surface of Venus. *Scientific American* (December), pp. 60-65.

Saunders, R.S. et al. (1992) Magellan Mission Summary. *Journal of Geophysical Research,* Vol. 97, No. E8 (August 25), pp. 13,067-13,090.

Smith, B.A. (1990) Voyage of the century. *National Geographic,* August. (Describes the voyager missions.)

Swindle, Timothy D., Lewis, John S., and McFadden, Lucy-Ann A. (1991) The case for planetary sample return missions: 4. Near-Earth asteroids and the history of planetary formation. *EOS,* Vol. 72, No. 44 (October 29), pp. 473, 479-480.

Taylor, Stuart Ross (1987) The origin of the Moon. *American Scientist,* Vol. 75 (September-October), pp. 469-477.

THE EARTH BENEATH OUR FEET

Books & Reports:

Bolt, Bruce A. (1992) *Earthquakes.* New York: W.H. Freeman & Co.

Dietrich, R., and Skinner, B. (1990) *Gems, Granites and Gravels: Knowing and Using Rocks and Minerals.* Cambridge: Cambridge University Press.

Moores, E.M., ed. (1990) *Shaping the Earth: Tectonics of Continents and Oceans.* Scientific American Readings. New York: W.H. Freeman & Co.

National Research Council, Committee on Status and Research Objectives in the Solid-Earth Sciences (1993) *Solid-Earth Sciences and Society.* Washington: National Academy Press.

Simarski, L.T. (1992) *Volcanism and Climate Change.* American Geophysical Union Special Report.

Skinner, Brian J., and Porter, Stephen C. (1995) *The Dynamic Earth.* 3rd edition. New York: John Wiley & Sons.

Tilling, Robert I. (1988) *How Volcanoes Work.* American Geophysical Union.

Wright, Thomas L., and Pierson, T.C. (1992) *Living with Volcanoes.* US Geological Survey Circular 1073, US Geological Survey Box 25424, Federal Center, Denver, CO 80225.

Articles:

Bolt, Bruce A. (1987) Fifty years of studies on the inner core. *EOS* (February 10), pp. 73, 80-82.

Borchardt, Glenn (1991) Preparation and use of earthquake planning scenarios. *California Geology,* Vol. 4, No. 3, pp. 195-203.

Brown, V.M., and Harrell, J.A. (1991) Megascopic classification of rocks. *Journal of Geological Education,* Vol. 39, p. 379.

Dewees, D.N. (1987) Does the danger from asbestos in buildings warrant the cost of taking it out? *American Scientist,* Vol. 75 (May-June), pp. 285-288.

Howell, B.F. Jr. (1986) History of ideas on the cause of earthquakes. *EOS* (November 18), pp.1323-1326.

King, G., Bailey, G., and Sturdy, D. (1994) Active tectonics, topography, and human survival tactics. *Journal of Geophysical Research,* Vol. 99.

Lay, Thorne, Ahrens, Thomas J., Olson, Peter, Smyth, Joseph, and Loper, David (1990) Studies of the Earth's interior: Goals and trends. *Physics Today* (October), pp. 44-52.

Lewis, Trevor, and Wang, Kevin (1992) Geothermal research related to past climate. *EOS,* Vol. 73, No. 25 (June 23), pp. 265, 269

Poulson, Howard, Card, Ken, Mortensen, Jim, and Robert, François (1992) *Plate tectonics and the mineral wealth of the Canadian Shield.* Geotimes (August), pp. 19-21.

Rampino, Michael R. (1989) Distant effects of the Tambora eruption of April 1815. *EOS* (December 19).

Simarski, Lynn Teo (1992) Volcanism and climate change. *Earth in Space,* Vol. 4, No. 9 (May), pp. 5-10.

Snider, Frederic G. (1990) Eastern US earthquakes: Assessing the hazard. Geotimes (November), pp. 13-15.

Wuethrich, Bernice (1994) California earthquake assessed. *Earth in Space,* Vol. 6, No. 6 (February), pp. 5-7.

THE EARTH'S BLANKET OF WATER AND ICE

Books & Reports:

Brown, Lester R., and Wolf, Edward C. (1984) *Soil Erosion: Quiet Crisis in the World Economy.* Worldwatch Paper 60. Worldwatch Institute.

Duxbury, Alyn C., and Duxbury, Alison B. (1994) *An Introduction to the World's Oceans.* Dubuque, IA: William C. Brown, 4th ed.

Dawson, Alastair G. (1991) *Ice Age Earth.* Routledge.

Solley, W.B., Pierce, R.R., and Perlman, Howard A. (1993) *Estimated Use of Water in the United States in 1990.* Washington: US Geological Survey Circular 1081.

US Government Report (1990) *Coping With An Oiled Sea: An Analysis of Oil Spill Response.* Available from Superintendent of Documents, US Government Printing Office (GPO), Washington, DC 20402-9325 Tel: (202) 783-3238.

White, Catherine (1993) The Great Flood of 1993. *Earth in Space,* Vol. 6, No. 2 (October), pp. 7-10.

Williams, J.S., Dodd, K., and Gohn, Kathleen (1990) *Coasts in crisis.* US Geological Survey Circular 1075.

Articles:

Carrier, J. (1991) The Colorado: A river run dry. *National Geographic,* June.

Ebbesmeyer, Curtis, and Ingraham, W. James (1994) Pacific toy spill fuels ocean current pathways research. *Earth in Space,* Vol. 7, No. 2 (October), pp. 7-9, 14 (from an article that appeared in *EOS,* Vol. 75, p. 425, September 13, 1994).

Fyfe, W. S. (1989) Soil and global change. *Episodes,* Vol. 12, No. 4 (December), pp. 249-254.

Hall, Dorothy K., Williams, Richard S., and Bayr, Klaus J. (1992) Glacier recession in Iceland and Austria. *EOS,* Vol. 73, No. 12, March 24, pp. 129, 135-137.

Hokkaido Tsunami Survey Group (1993) Tsunami devastates Japanese coastal region. *Earth in Space,* Vol. 5, No. 4 (December), pp. 8-10.

Jeffries, Martin O. (1993) Arctic ice shelves and islands. *Earth in Space,* Vol. 5, No. 3 (November), pp. 10-11 (adapted from an article in the August 1992 *Reviews of Geophysics*).

Leatherman, Stephen P., and Dean, Robert G. (1991) Beach erosion rates and the National Flood Insurance Program. *EOS,* Vol. 72, No. 2 (January 8), pp. 9, 16.

Lehman, S.J., and Keigwin, L.D. (1992) Deep circulation revisited. *Nature,* Vol. 358, pp. 197-198.

Molnia, Bruce (1993) Bering Glacier starts major surge. *Earth in Space,* Vol. 6, No. 1 (September), pp. 10-11.

National Academy of Sciences (1991) Water's central role in the Earth system. Earth in Space, Vol. 3, No. 9 (May), pp. 5-7, 14 (excerpted from *Opportunities in the Hydrologic Sciences* (1991) National Academy Press).

National Geographic (1993) Water: The power, promise and turmoil of North America's fresh water. *National Geographic* Special Edition, November.

Philander, George (1989) El Niño and La Niña. *American Scientist,* Vol. 77 (September-October), pp. 451-459.

Ramage, Colin S. (1986) El Niño. *Scientific American* (June), p. 76.

Rasmussen, Eugene M. (1985) El Niño and variations in climate. *American Scientist,* Vol. 73 (March-April), pp. 168-177.

Robigou, Véronique, and Ballard, Robert D. (1994) Deep-sea study takes a new approach. *Earth in Space,* Vol. 6, No. 6 (February), pp. 8-11.

Thomson, Richard (1993) Future droughts, water shortages in parts of western Europe. *Earth in Space,* Vol. 5, No. 8 (April), pp. 8-9, 14.

der Veen, C.J. (1993) Ice sheets: Growing or shrinking? *Earth in Space,* Vo. 5, No. 5 (January), pp. 5-9).

Woods Hole Oceanographic Institute (1993) Coastal science and policy I. *Oceanus,* Vol. 36, No. 1.

Zwingle, E. (1993) Ogallala aquifer: Well spring of the High Plains. *National Geographic,* March.

THE EARTH'S GASEOUS ENVELOPE

Books & Reports:

American Geophysical Union (1989) *Understanding Climate Change.* Geophysical Monograph Series, Vol. 52.

Barry, Roger G., and Chorley, Richard J. (1992) *Atmosphere, Weather and Climate.* Routledge.

Graedel, T.E., and Paul J. Crutzen (1992) *Atmospheric Change: An Earth Systems Perspective.* New York: W.H. Freeman & Co.

Hidore, John J., and Oliver, John E. (1993) *Climatology: An Atmospheric Science.* New York: Macmillan Publishing.

Houghton, J.T., Jenkins, G.J., and Ephraums, J.J., eds. (1990) *The Intergovernmental Panel on Climate Change Scientific Assessment.* Cambridge: Cambridge University Press.

National Research Council (1989) *Ozone Depletion, Greenhouse Gases, and Climate Change.* Proceedings of a Joint Symposium by the Board of Atmospheric Sciences and Climate and the Committee on Global Change, National Research Council. Washington: National Academy Press.

Articles:

Andreae, Meinrat O. (1993) Global distribution of fires seen from space. *Earth in Space,* Vol. 5, No. 7 (March), pp. 12-14 (excerpted from an article in the March 23 1993 issue of *EOS*).

Ausubel, Jesse H. (1991) A second look at the impacts of climate change. *American Scientist,* Vol. 79 (May-June), pp. 210-221.

Broecker, W.S. (1994) Is Earth climate poised to jump again? *Geotimes* (November) pp. 16-18. (This entire issue of Geotimes is devoted to the subject of global change.)

Broecker, W.S., and Denton. G.H. (1990) What drives glacial cycles. *Scientific American,* January, 43-50.

Davis, Robert E., and Dolan, Robert (1993) Nor'easters. *American Scientist,* Vol. 81 (September-October), pp. 428-439.

Greenland Ice Sheet Project (1994) Record drilling depth struck in Greenland. *Earth in Space,* Vol. 6, No. 7 (March), pp. 10-14.

Hobbs, Peter V. (1994) Clouds: Their beauty and challenge. *Earth in Space,* Vol. 6, No. 9 (May), pp. 6-8.

Houghton, Richard A., and Woodwell, George M. (1989) Global climatic change. *Scientific American,* Vol. 260, No. 4 (April), pp. 36-44.

Hulme, Mike, and Kelly, Mick (1993) Exploring the links between desertification and climate change. Environment, Vol. 35, No. 6 (July-August), pp. 5-11, 39-45.

Keith, David W., and Dowlatabadi, Hadi (1993) A serious look at geoengineering. *Earth in Space,* Vol. 5, No. 6 (February), pp. 5-7 (excerpted from an article in the Jun 7, 1992 issue of *EOS*).

Levine, Joel S. (1990) The consequences of global biomass burning. *EOS,* September 11.

Maranto, Gina (1993) Gone with the wind (Hurricane Andrew). *Discover* (January).

Michaels, Patrick J. (1992) *Sound and Fury: The Science and Politics of Global Warming.* CATO Institute.

National Academy of Sciences (1991) The discovery of the Antarctic ozone hole. *Earth in Space,* Vol. 3, No. 7 (March), pp. 10-14 (adapted from *One Earth, One Future* (1989) National Academy Press).

National Ocenaographic and Atmospheric Administration (1993) Nature's most violent storms. *Earth in Space,* Vol. 5, No. 6 (February), pp. 8-9 (excerpted from *Tornadoes...Nature's Most Violent Storms* (1992) National Oceanographic and Atmospheric Administration, Federal Emergency Management Agency and American Red Cross (September).

Newton, David E. (1993) *Global Warming: A Reference Handbook.* Santa Barbara, CA: ABC-CLIO.

Nordhaus, W. (1994) Expert opinion on climate change. *American Scientist,* vol. 82, pp. 45-51.

Risby, James S., Handel, Mark David, and Stone, Peter H. (1991) Should we delay responses to the greenhouse issue? EOS, Vol. 72, No. 53 (December 31), p. 593.

Self, Stephen, and Rampino, Michael R. (1988) The relationship between volcanic eruptions and climate change: Still a conundrum? *EOS* (February 9), pp. 74-75, 85-86.

Trefil, James (1990) Modeling Earth's future climate requires both science and guesswork. Smithsonian (December) Vol. 21, No. 9, pp. 29-37.

Wuethrich, Bernice (1994) Predicting future climate. *Earth in Space,* Vol. 6, No. 7 (March), p. 8.

THE DYNAMICS OF LIFE ON EARTH

Books & Reports:

Brum, G.H., McKane, Larry, and Karp, Gerry (1994) *Biology: Exploring Life.* New York: John Wiley & Sons, 2nd. ed.

Gould, Stephen J. (1989) *Wonderful Life: The Burgess Shale and the Nature of History.* New York: W.W. Norton.

Margulis, Lynn, and Olendzenski, Lorraine, eds. (1992) *Environmental Evolution: Effects of the Origin and Evolution of Life on Planet Earth.* Cambridge: The MIT Press.

Nisbet, E.G. (1992) *Living Earth: A Short History of Life and Its Home.* Unwin Hyman Academic.

Ryan, John C. (1992) *Life Support: Conserving Biological Diversity.* Worldwatch Paper 108. Worldwatch Institute.

Wilson, E.O., ed. (1988) *Biodiversity.* Washington: National Academy Press.

Zepp, Richard G., ed. (1994) *Climate-Biosphere Interactions: Biogenic Emissions and Environmental Effects of Climate Change.* John Wiley & Sons.

Articles:

Briggs, Derek E.G. (1991) Extraordinary fossils. *American Scientist,* Vol. 79, No. 2, p. 133.

Ehrenfeld, D. (1986) Thirty million cheers for diversity. *NewScientist,* Vol. 110, pp. 38-43.

Fenchel, Tom, and Finlay, Bland J. (1994) The evolution of life without oxygen. *American Scientist,* Vol. 82 (January-February), pp. 22-29.

Gensel, Patricia G., and Andrews, Henry N. (1987) The evolution of early land plants. *American Scientist,* Vol. 75 (September-October), pp. 478-487.

Glen, William (1990) What killed the dinosaurs? *American Scientist,* Vol. 78 (July-August), pp. 354-370.

Graham, Linda E. (1985) The origin of the life cycle of land plants. *American Scientist,* Vol. 73 (March-April), pp. 178-183.

Gray, Jane, and Shear, William (1992) Early life on land. *American Scientist,* Vol. 80 (September-October), pp. 444-456.

May, R.M. (1986) How many species are there? *Nature,* Vol. 324, pp. 514-515.

Montgomery, R.S., and Strong, A.E. (1994) Coral bleaching threatens ocean, life. *Earth in Space,* Vol. 6, No. 9 (May), pp. 12-14.

Nicol, Stephen, and del la Mare, William (1993) Ecosystem management and the Antarctic krill. American Scientist, Vol. 81 (January-February), pp. 36-41.

Raup, D.M. (1986) Biological extinction in Earth history. *Science,* Vol. 231, pp. 1528-1533.

Raup, D.M., and Sepkoski, J.J. Jr. (1984) Periodicity of extinctions in the geologic past. Proc. Natl. Acad. Sci. USA 81:801-805.

Sepkoski, J. John Jr. (1994) Extinction and the fossil record. *Geotimes* (March), pp. 15-17.

Shock, Everett L. (1994) Hydrothermal systems and the emergence of life. *Geotimes* (March), pp. 12-14.

Simberloff, D. (1986) Are we on the verge of a mass extinction in tropical rain forests? Pp. 165-180 in Elliott, D.K., ed., *Dynamics of Extinction.* New York: John Wiley & Sons.

White, M. Catherine (1993) What killed the dinosaurs? *Earth in Space,* Vol. 5, No. 4, pp. 5-7.

Wilson, E.O. (1985) The biological diversity crisis: A challenge to science. Issues Sci. Technol. Vol. 2, No. 1, pp. 20-29.

Wolf, E.C. (1985) Conserving biological diversity. Pp. 124-126 in Brown, L. et al., eds. *The State of the World 1985.* New York: W.W. Norton & Co.

LIVING ON THE EARTH

Books & Reports:

Craig, James R., Vaughan, David J., and Skinner, Brian J. (1988) *Resources of the Earth.* Englewood Cliffs, NJ: Prentice-Hall.

Flavin, Christopher, and Nicholas Lenssen (1994) *Power Surge: Guide to the Coming Energy Revolution.* Washington: Worldwatch Institute.

Mungall, Constance, and Digby J. McLaren, eds. (1990) *Planet Under Stress: The Challenge of Global Change.* Toronto: Oxford University Press.

Nisbet, E.G. (1991) *Leaving Eden: To Protect and Manage the Earth.* Cambridge: Cambridge University Press.

Nuhfer, Edward B., Proctor, Richard J., and Moser, Paul H. (1993) *The Citizens' Guide to Geologic Hazards.* The American Institute of Professional Geologists.

Scientific American (1990) *Managing planet Earth: Readings from Scientific American.* New York: Freeman.

Skinner, Brian J. (1986) *Earth Resources.* Englewood Cliffs, NJ: Prentice-Hall.

Tolba, Mostafa K., El-Kholy, Osama A., El-Hinnawi, E., Holdgate, M.W., McMichael, D.F., and Munn, R.E., eds. (1992) *The World Environment 1972-1992: Two Decades of Challenge.* London: Chapmen & Hall (United Nations Environment Programme).

Turner, B.L., Clark, William C., Kates, Robert W., Richards, John F., Mathews, Jessica T., and Meyer, William B., eds. (1993) *The Earth as Transformed by Human Action: Global and Regional Changes in the Biosphere Over the Past 300 Years.* Cambridge University Press.

World Resources Institute (1994) *World Resources: A Guide to the Global Environment.* Oxford: Oxford University Press.

Wyman, Richard L., ed. (1991) *Global Climate Change and Life on Earth.* New York: Chapman & Hall.

Youngquist, W. (1990) *Mineral Resources and the Destinies of Nations.* Portland, OR: National Book Company.

Articles:

Ahearne, John F. (1993) The future of nuclear power. *American Scientist,* Vol. 81 (January-February), pp. 24-35.

Bookout, John C. (1989) Two centuries of fossil fuel energy. *Episodes,* Vol. 12, No. 4 (December), pp. 257-262.

Kowalok, Michael E., (1993) Research lessons from acid rain, ozone depletion, and global warming. *Environment,* Vol. 35, No. 6 (July-August), pp. 12-38.

Rathje, William J. (1991) Once and future landfills. *National Geographic,* May.

Scientific American (1990) Energy for planet Earth. *Scientific American* Special Issue, September.

Skinner, Brian J. (1989) Resources in the 21st century: Can supplies meet needs? *Episodes,* Vol. 12, No. 4 (December), pp. 267-275.

US National Committee for the Decade for Natural Disaster Reduction, National Research Council (1993) The Decade for Natural Disaster Reduction. *Earth in Space,* Vol. 5, No. 5 (January) pp. 10-14 (excerpted from *A Safer Future: Reducing the Impacts of Natural Disasters* (1991) Washington: National Academy Press).

Young, John E. (1992) Mining the Earth. In Brown, Lester R., et al., *State of the World 1992: A Worldwatch Institute Report.* New York: W.W. Norton & Co., 100-118.

EARTH SYSTEM SCIENCE—GENERAL

Books & Reports:

Brown, Lester, et al., eds. *State of the World.* New York: W.W. Norton & Co. (updated yearly).

Carter, T.R., Parry, M.L., Nishioka, S., and Harasawa, H., eds. (1992) *Preliminary Guidelines for Assessing the Impacts of Climate Change.* Environmental Change Unit (UK) and Center for Global Environmental Research (Japan) for Working Group of the Intergovernmental Panel on Climate Change.

Emiliani, Cesare (1992) *Planet Earth and Cosmology, Geology, and the Evolution of Life and Environment.* Cambridge: Cambridge University Press.

Gould, Stephen J. (1987) *Time's Arrow, Time's Cycle: Myth and Metaphor in the Discovery of Geological Time.* Cambridge, MA: Harvard University Press.

International Geosphere-Biosphere Programme (ongoing, starting in 1986) Report Series. The series includes titles such as *Global Changes of the Past* (No. 6, 1989), *Effects of Atmospheric and Climate Change on Terrestrial Ecosystems* (No. 5, 1989), and *The Land-Atmosphere Interface* (No. 10, 1989). Available from IGBP Secretariat, The Royal Swedish Academy of Sciences, Box 50005, S-104 05 Stockholm, Sweden Tel: (+46-8) 16 64 48 Fax: (+46-8) 16 64 05.

International Geosphere-Biosphere Programme (1992) *Global Change: Reducing Uncertainties.* The Royal Swedish Academy of Sciences, Box 50005, S-104 05 Stockholm, Sweden Tel: (+46-8) 16 64 48 Fax: (+46-8) 16 64 05.

NASA (1988) *Earth System Science: A Program for Global Change.* Report of the Earth System Sciences Committee. Office for Interdisciplinary Earth Studies, University Corporation for Atmospheric Research, PO Box 3000, Boulder, CO 80307.

Schlesinger, W.H. (1991) *Biogeochemistry: An Analysis of Global Change.* San Diego, CA: Academic Press.

Sharpton, V.L., and P.E. Ward (1991) *Global Catastrophes in Earth History: An Interdisciplinary Conference on Impacts, Volcanism, and Mass Mortality.* Geological Society of America Special Paper 247.

Articles:

Committee on Status and Research Objectives in the Solid-Earth Sciences (1993) Our understanding of the Earth has just begun. *Earth in Space,* Vol. 5, No. 7 (March), pp. 5-10 (excerpted from *Solid Earth Sciences and Society* (1993) National Academy of Sciences).

Committee on Status and Research Objectives in the Solid-Earth Sciences (1993) The dynamic Earth. *Earth in Space,* Vol. 5, No. 8 (April), pp. 12-14 (excerpted from *Solid Earth Sciences and Society* (1993) National Academy of Sciences).

Committee on Status and Research Objectives in the Solid-Earth Sciences (1993) The global environment and its evolution. *Earth in Space,* Vol. 5, No. 9 (May), pp. 10-11, 14 (excerpted from *Solid Earth Sciences and Society* (1993) National Academy of Sciences).

Eden, H.F., Elero, B.P., and Perkins, J.N. (1993) Nimbus satellites set the stage for mission to Planet Earth. *Earth in Space,* Vol. 6, No. 1 (September), pp. 12-14 (excerpted from an article that appeared in the June 29, 1993 issue of *EOS*).

Physics Today (1994) Physics and the environment. *Physics Today,* Special Issue, November.

Wuethrich, Bernice (1993) El Niño and the volcano in 1992. *Earth in Space,* Vol. 5, No. 3 (November), pp. 13-14.

SUPPLEMENTS

OVERVIEW

A full range of publishers supplements is available to accompany *The Blue Planet*. This includes a *Laboratory Manual* and *Instructor's Guide for the Laboratory Manual; CD-ROM; Computerized Test Bank;* and *Study Guide* for students. These supplements are described in detail on page viii of the text. Following is a complete description of the *Earth Science Overhead Transparencies* and *Earth Science Slide Sets*.

EARTH SCIENCE OVERHEAD TRANSPARENCY/SLIDE SET

This set of full-colour overhead transparencies and the matching set of slides include 73 line drawings and tables from the text, edited for classroom application. The left-hand column indicates the number of the corresponding figure in the text.

Fig. #

CI.1 1. Energy reaches the Earth's surface from three sources: the Sun, the Earth's interior, and the tides. The Earth is such a dynamic planet because these three energy sources drive different activities. Internal heat drives all of the solid Earth's internal activities, such as mountain building and volcanism. The Sun's energy and, to a much smaller extent, the tides drive all of the external activities, such as erosion, wind, ocean currents, and the growth of green plants.

1.13 2. A sliced view of the Earth reveals layers of different composition and zones of different rock strength. The compositional layers, starting from the inside, are the core, the mantle, and the crust. Note that the crust is thicker under the continents than under the oceans. Note, too, that boundaries between zones of different physical properties—lithosphere (outermost), asthenosphere, mesosphere—do not coincide with compositional boundaries.

2.6 3. A model of the Sun's interior. Energy is created in the core when hydrogen is fused to helium. This energy flows out from the core by radiation through the radiative layer, by convection through the convective layer, and by radiation from the surface of the photosphere, which is the portion of the Sun we see.

2.11 4. The outer-space and sea-level spectra of solar radiation. The two curves are different because gases in the atmosphere selectively absorb some of the wavelengths of emitted radiation.

2.13   5.   The sunspot cycle over the past 400 years. Note the period before 1715, when, for reasons that are not understood, very few sunspots were observed. Sunspots have reached a maximum about every 11 years since 1715, and there is also a suggestion of some sort of cycle on a 55- to 57-year time scale. Because the pre-1715 period of low sunspot activity coincides with a prolonged cool period that is sometimes called the Little Ice Age, some scientists have speculated that sunspot activity and climate are somehow connected.

3.7   6.   Travel paths of direct and refracted body waves from shallow focus earthquake to nearby seismograph station.

C3.1   7.   Measurements used for determining the Richter magnitude (M) from a seismograph record.

4.4   8.   The tetrahedron-shaped silicate anion $(SiO_4)^{4-}$. A. Anion with the four oxygens touching each other in natural position. Silicon (dashed circle) occupies central space. B. Exploded view showing the relatively large oxygen anions at the four corners of the tetrahedron, equidistant from the relatively small silicon cation.

4.6   9.   Summary of the way silicate anions polymerize to form the common silicate minerals. The most important polymerizations are those that produce chains, sheets, and three-dimensional networks. Note the relationship between crystal structure and cleavage.

5.7   10.   Sequence of events leading to the eruption of Mount St. Helens on May 18, 1980. Time approximately 0s: Earthquakes and then puffs of steam and ash indicate that magma is rising: the north face of the mountain bulges alarmingly. Time approximately 40s: an earthquake shakes the mountain, and the bulge breaks loose and slides downward. This reduces the pressure on the magma and initiates the lateral blast. Time approximately 50s: the violence of the eruption causes a second block to slide downward, exposing more of the magma and initiating an eruption column. Time approximately 60s: the eruption increases in intensity. The eruption column carries volcanic ash as high as 19 km into the atmosphere.

5.12   11.   Sequence of events that formed Crater Lake following the eruption of Mount Mazama 6600 years ago. A. An eruption column of tephra rises from the flank of Mount Mazama. B. The eruption reaches a climax. Dense clouds of ash fill the air, and the hot pyroclastic flows sweep down the mountain side. C. the top of Mount Mazama collapses into the partly empty magma chamber, forming a caldera 10 km in diameter. D. During a final phase of eruption, Wizard Island formed.

5.17   12.   Bowen's reaction series demonstrates how the cooling and crystallization of a primary magma of basaltic composition, through reactions between mineral grains and magma followed by separation of mineral grains and magma, can change from basaltic to andesitic to rhyolitic. Bowen identified two series of reactions: a continuous series in which one mineral, feldspar, changes from an initial calcium-rich form to a sodium-rich one; and a discontinuous series in which minerals change abruptly—for example, from olivine to pyroxene.

5.18   13.   Diagram illustrating the locations of the major kinds of volcanoes in a plate tectonic setting.

6.9   14.   The Earth's seismicity outlines plate margins. This map shows earthquakes of magnitude 4.0 or greater from 1960 to 1989. Six large plates of lithosphere and several smaller ones are present. Each plate moves slowly but steadily in the direction shown by the arrows.

C6.4   15.   Hawaiian chain of volcanoes, showing the oldest reliable ages (in millions of years). The age increases from southeast to northwest.

6.16   16.   Schematic diagram showing the major features of a plate. Near the spreading center, where the temperature is high because of rising magma, the lithosphere is thin. Away from the spreading center, the lithosphere cools, becomes denser and also thicker, and so the lithosphere-asthenosphere boundary is deeper. When the lithosphere sinks into the asthenosphere at the subduction zone, it is reheated. At a depth of about 100 km, the oceanic crust starts to melt, and the magma rises and forms an acruate belt of andesitic stratovolcanoes parallel to the subduction zone.

7.2   17.   Sequence of geologic events leading to the three kinds of unconformity: (1) nonconformity; (2) angular unconformity; and (3) disconformity.

C7.1   18.   Curves illustrating the basic law of radioactivity. A. At time zero, a sample consists of 100 percent radioactive parent atoms. During each time unit, half the atoms remaining decay to daughter atoms. B. At time zero, no daughter atoms are present. After one time unit corresponding to a half-life of the parent atoms,

50 percent of the sample has been converted to daughter atoms. After two time units, 75 percent of the sample is daughter atoms and 25 percent parent atoms. After three time units, the percentages are 87.5 and 12.5, respectively. Note that at any given instant N_p, the number of parent atoms remaining, plus N_d, the number of daughter atoms, equals N_0, the number of parent atoms at time zero.

7.14   19. Metamorphic facies plotted with respect to temperature and pressure. Curve A is a typical thermal gradient around an intrusive igneous rock that causes low-pressure metamorphism. Curve B is a normal continental geothermal gradient. Curve C is the geothermal gradient developed in a subduction zone.

7.15   20. Diagram of a convergent plate boundary, showing the different regions of metamorphism. Dashed lines indicate temperature contours.

7.16   21. The North American cratons and associated orogens. The Grenville orogen is about 1 billion years old, while the Caledonide, Appalachian, Cordilleran, and Innuitian orogens are each younger than 600 million years. The assemblage of cratons and orogens, all older than 1.8 billion years, which are surrounded by the five young orogens, is the Canadian Shield.

7.20   22. Collision between two fragments of continental crust shown schematically for the collision between India and Tibet. A. India, on the left, moves north. Sixty million years ago an ocean still separated India and Tibet. B. India and Tibet start to collide about 40 million years ago. Sediment is buckled and fractured, and the lithosphere is thickened. C. The collision starts to elevate the Himalaya about 20 million years ago. The downward-moving plate of lithosphere capped by oceanic crust breaks off and continues to sink. D. The edge of the remaining segment of the plate on which India sits, and which is capped by buoyant continental crust, is partly thrust under the edge of the overriding plate on which Tibet sits, causing further elevation of the collision zone. The process is continuing and the Himalaya are still rising.

8.7   23. Depth zones in the ocean. Below the surface zone lies another zone in which the ocean-water properties experience a significant change with increasing depth. This zone is variously known as A. the pycnocline, a zone of increasing density; B. the thermocline, a zone of decreasing temperature; C. the halocline, a zone of increasing salinity. Still lower lies the deep zone, where waters are dense as a result of their low temperatures and high salinity.

8.8   24. Coriolis Effect A. A body at the pole rotates completely around every 24 hours while a body on the equator goes end-over-end but does not rotate. The face on the tower at the pole rotates with respect to an external observer whereas a tower on the equator always presents the same face to an observer. B. On the rotating Earth, an object freely floating on the ocean in the northern hemisphere (a, b) is deflected by the Coriolis effect to the right, whereas in the southern hemisphere (c, d) it is deflected to the left. A moving object at the equator (e, f) is not deflected.

8.9   25.   Surface ocean currents form a distinctive pattern, curving to the right (clockwise) in the northern hemisphere and to the left (counterclockwise) in the southern hemisphere. the westward flow of tropical Atlantic and Pacific waters is interrupted by continents, which deflect the water poleward. The flow then turns away from the poles and becomes the eastward-moving currents that define the middle-latitude margins of the five great midocean gyres.

8.12   26.   Geostrophic flow. A. The Coriolis effect causes major wind-driven surface currents to be deflected toward the middle of a gyre where water plies up to form a gentle mound above the average level of the ocean. In this diagram, the vertical scale is greatly exaggerated. The water plies up until the force of gravity (Fg) pulling the water downslope just balances the Coriolis effect (Fc). The net result is geostrophic flow (GF) around the gyre. B. Geostrophic flow in the subtropical North Atlantic traps a broad lens of clear water a kilometer deep, forming the Sargasso Sea.

8.13A   27.   Transect along the western Atlantic Ocean showing water masses and general circulation pattern. North Atlantic Deep Water (NADW) originates near the surface in the North Atlantic as northward-flowing surface water cools, becomes increasingly saline, and plunges to depths of several km. As NADW moves into the South Atlantic, it rises over denser Antarctic Bottom Water (AABW), which forms adjacent to the Antarctic continent and flows into the North Atlantic as Antarctic Intermediate Water (AAIW) at a mean depth of about 1 km.

8.13B   28.   The major thermohaline circulation cells that make up the global ocean conveyor system are driven by exchange of heat and moisture between the atmosphere and ocean. Dense water forming at a number of sites in the North Atlantic spreads slowly along the ocean floor, eventually to enter both the Indian and Pacific oceans before slowly upwellng and entering shallower parts of the thermohaline circulation cells. Antarctic Bottom Water (AABW) forms adjacent to Antarctica and flows northward in fresher, colder circulation cells beneath warmer, more saline waters in the South Atlantic and South Pacific. It also flows along the

Southern Ocean beneath the Antarctic Circumpolar Current to enter the southern Indian Ocean. Warm surface waters flowing into the western Atlantic and Pacific basins close the great global thermohaline cells.

8.23   29.   Tidal forces. A. Tide-raising forces are produced by the Moon's gravitational attraction and by inertial force. On the side toward the Moon, both forces combine to distort the water level from that of a sphere, raising a tidal bulge. On the opposite side of the Earth, where inertial force is greater than the gravitational force of the Moon, the excess inertial force (called the tide-raising force) also creates a tidal bulge. B. The horizontal component of the tide-raising force is shown by arrows on an oblique view of the Earth. The arrows are directed toward the point where a line connecting the Earth and Moon intersects the Earth's surface. this point shifts latitude with time as the relative position of the Earth and Moon change.

9.16   30.   Evolution of a drainage network in an experimental rainfall-erosion container. The initial channel, which directed runoff toward the lower end of the container, grew headward and developed new tributaries as it spread to encompass the drainage basin.

9.23   31.   Two conditions are necessary for an artesian system: a confined aquifer and water pressure sufficient to make the water in a well rise above the aquifer. The water in a nonartesian well rises to the same height as the water table in the recharge area (line AB), minus an amount determined by the loss of energy in friction of percolation. Thus, the water can rise only to the line AC, which slopes downward and away from the recharge area. In the artesian well downslope, water flows out at the surface without pumping, for the well top lies below line AC.

10.4   32.   Contours (in meters) show the regional altitude of the snowline throughout northwestern United States, British Columbia, and southern Alaska for a representative balance year. The surface defined by the contours rises steeply inland from the Pacific coast in response to increasingly drier climate, and also from north to south in response to progressively higher mean annual temperatures.

10.12   33.   Main features of a valley glacier. The glacier has been cut away along its center line so that only half is shown. Crevasses form where the glacier flows over an abruptly steepened slope. Arrows show the local directions of ice flow. A band of rock debris forms a medial moraine that marks the boundary between the main glacier and a tributary glacier joining it from a lateral valley.

10.13   34.   Maps of South Cascade Glacier in the Washington Cascade Range at the end of two successive balance years showing the position of the equilibrium line relative to the position it would have under a balanced condition. The curves plot mass balance as a function of altitude. During the first year, A, a negative balance year, the glacier lost mass and the equilibrium line was high (2025 m). The following year, B, a positive balance year, the glacier gained mass and the equilibrium line was low (1800 m).

10.19   35.   Season extent of sea ice in A. southern hemisphere and B. northern hemisphere.

10.20   36.   Seasonal variations in the sea-ice cover around Antarctica in a typical year. The ice is least extensive during the summer months (January-March) but steadily increases, reaching a maximum in winter (July-September). At the time of maximum sea ice (September), a large polynya has developed northeast of the Weddell Sea.

11.5   37.   Soils vary across the landscape, as shown by this example of three soil profiles from forest, grassland, and desert regions. Differences are explainable in terms of regolith composition, slope steepness, vegetation cover, soil biota, climate, and the time required to develop the profile.

11.9   38.   Map of the western hemisphere showing the location of major drainage divides. The continental divide separating streams draining to the Pacific, Arctic, and Gulf of Mexico in North America and to the Pacific and Atlantic in South America follows the crest of the high cordillera in both hemispheres. In eastern North America, the divide separating Atlantic and Gulf of Mexico drainage follows the Appalachian Mountains and much of the limit of ice sheet glaciation south of the Great Lakes.

11.26   39.   Cross section through a barchan dune showing the typical gentle windward slope and steep slip face. Sand grains saltate up the windward slope to the top to the slip face where they accumulate and then avalanche downward. Cross-bedded strata inside the dune represent old slip faces.

C11.1   40.   Uplift rate across a mountain range calculated using fission-track ages. A. Two million years ago, a zircon crystal (A) in a cooling pluton passes the closure isotherm of 240°C and begins to acquire fission tracks. Another crystal (B) began acquiring tracks 2 million years earlier and since then has been uplifted 1200 m above the 240°C isotherm. B. Rock samples containing zircon crystals A and B collected from a stream valley eroded into the rising mountain range have fission track ages of 2 and 4 million years, respectively, and lie 6000 and 2400 m, respectively, above the closure isotherm of 240°C. C. by using these data, the average uplift of samples A and B are calculated as 2.5 and 0.6 mm/year, respectively.

12.4   41.   Life-protecting layers of O, O_2, and O_3 in the atmosphere absorb lethal ultraviolet radiation.

12.15   42.   As an unsaturated mass of air rises, it expands and cools at the dry adiabatic lapse rate (10°C/km). When the air temperature falls to the point where the air is saturated, condensation commences and latent heat is released. A further increase in altitude causes more condensation and the release of more latent heat; the air temperature now decreases at the moist adiabatic lapse rate (6°C/km). Note that the speed with which the air rises does not necessarily change; what changes is the temperature drop with altitude. Shown beside the curve are the volumes of a mass of rising air that starts as a cube 1 km on an edge.

12.19   43.   The altitudes of clouds. An anvil head is the flattened top of a cumulonimbus cloud that spreads across the top of the troposphere.

13.5   44.   A geostrophic wind. A high-altitude wind is deflected by the Coriolis effect until a balance is reached between the direction of flow due to the pressure gradient and the direction due to the Coriolis deflection, at which point flow is parallel to the isobars.

13.7   45.   Air spirals into a low and out from a high. Lows are centers of convergence, while highs are centers of divergence. Note that, in both lows and highs, the flow direction is oblique to the isobars because of friction.

13.9   46.   A. Convergence in a cyclone causes a rising updraft of air and with it clouds and probably precipitation. B. Divergence in an anticyclone draws in high-altitude air, creating a downdraft; clear skies and fair weather.

13.12   47.   The Earth's global wind system. Moist air, heated in the warm equatorial zone, rises convectively and forms clouds that produce abundant rain. Cool, dry air descending at latitudes 20-30° N and S produces a belt of subtropical high pressure in which lie many of the world's great deserts.

13.13   48.   The jet stream is a high-speed westerly geostrophic wind that occurs at the top of the troposphere over the polar front where a steep pressure gradient exists between cold polar air and warm subtropical air.

13.18   49.   Land and sea breezes. A. During the day, the land heats up more rapidly than does the sea. Air rises over the land, creating a low-pressure area. Cooler air flows in to this area from the sea, creating a sea breeze. B. During the night, the land cools more rapidly than the sea, and the reverse flow, a land breeze, occurs.

13.19   50.   Sources of the air masses that control the weather of North America.

14.1   51.   A diagrammatic representation of the Earth's climate system showing its five interacting components: lithosphere, atmosphere, oceans, cryosphere, and biosphere.

14.5   52.   Climate proxy records spanning all or part of the last 1000 years: A. frequency of major dustfall events in China (Source: After Zhang, 1982); B. severity of winters in England, recorded as the frequency of mild or severe months (Source: After Lamb, 1977); C. number of weeks per year during which sea ice reached the coast of Iceland (Source: After Lamb, 1977); D. freezing date of Lake Suwa in Japan relative to the long-term average (Source: After Lamb, 1966).

14.6   53.   Variations in the oxygen-isotope ratio through the Greenland Ice sheet. The zone of strong negative values beginning about 70,000 years ago and ending about 10,000 years marks the last glaciation. The sharp shift in values about 10,000 years ago marks an abrupt change from glacial to interglacial climate at the end of the glaciation.

14.14   54.   Changing distribution of spruce, hemlock, and elm trees in eastern North America at 6000-year intervals between the last glaciation (18,000 years ago) and the present day based on fossil pollen data. The color intensities indicate relative abundance for each species, with the darkest shade of green being the highest and the lightest shade the lowest.

14.21   55.   Geometry of the Earth's orbit and axial tilt. A. Precession. The Earth wobbles on its axis like a spinning top, making one revolution every 26,000 years. The axis of the Earth's elliptical orbit also rotates, though more slowly, in the opposite direction. These motions together cause a progressive shift, or precession, of the spring and autumn equinoxes, with each cycle lasting about 23,000 years. B. Tilt. The tilt of the Earth's axis, which is now about 23.5°, ranges from 21.5 to 24.5°, with each cycle lasting about 41,000 years. Increasing tilt means a greater difference, for each hemisphere, between the amount of solar radiation received in summer and that received in winter. C. Eccentricity. The Earth's orbit is an ellipse with the Sun at one focus. Over 100,000 years, the shape of the orbit changes from almost circular (low eccentricity) to more elliptical (high eccentricity). The higher the eccentricity, the greater the seasonal variation in radiation received at any point on the Earth's surface.

14.22   56.   Curves showing variations in eccentricity, tilt, and precession during the last 800,000 years. Summing these factors produces a combined signal that shows the amount of radiation received on the Earth at a particular latitude through time. The frequency of oscillations in the combined orbital signal closely matches that of the marine oxygen isotope curve which constitutes a proxy record of changing global ice volume.

14.23   57.   Curves comparing changes in carbon dioxide and methane with temperature changes based on oxygen-isotope values in samples from a deep ice core drilled at Vostok Station, Antarctica. Concentrations of these greenhouse gases were high during the early part of the last interglaciation, just as they are during the present interglaciation, but they were lower during glacial times. The curves are consistent with the hypothesis that these gases contributed to warm interglacial climates and cold glacial climates.

15.7   58.   Population cycles in the Canadian lynx and its prey, the snowshoe rabbit.

15.8   59.   Geometric representation of a niche. This example illustrates the temperature-salinity-depth tolerances that bound the niche of a reef-forming coral. The graph tells us that the water temperature ranges from 16 to 40°C, for instance, but coral thrives only between 20 and 36°C. The water salinity ranges from 20 to 45 parts per thousand, but the coral lives only when the salinity is between 29 and 41 parts per thousand.

15.9A,B   60.   Growth behavior of two species of Paramecium. A. Grown into separate cultures so there is no other niche competition. B. Mixed and grown in the same culture where they are competing for the same ecological niche. C. An example of a paramecium (Paramecium cordata). Paramecium are tiny, ranging in length from 0.07 to 0.30 mm.

C16.1   61.   The nitrogen cycle.

16.11   62.   The evolution of life on the Earth from 4.6 billion years ago to the present. The rates at which new organisms appear and of biological diversity both increase with time.

16.14   63.   Most of the fossils in the Burgess Shale of British Columbia are soft-bodied. Of the 25 different species depicted in the drawing, only the five circled had hard parts. The Burgess Shale is the most complete assemblage of Cambrian fauna ever found, and it is presumed that the abundance of soft-bodied animals reflected the situation elsewhere in the ocean. The most ancient chordate, Pikaia, is seen as a small fish.

16.20   64.   The extraordinary frequency of great extinction events that have occurred during the Phanerozoic Eon. The percentage of extinction was determined from the disappearance of genera of well-skeletonized animals.

17.13   65.   Locations of certain kinds of mineral deposits in terms of plate structures.

17.16   66.   The petroleum window is that combination of depth and temperature within which oil and gas are generated and trapped.

18.1   67.   Cumulative world population between 1700 and the present day obtained by summing values for each of the major inhabited regions of the world. Projected values extend the present estimates to the year 2020.

18.5   68.   Dramatic deforestation in Costa Rica between 1940 and 1983 reduced the percentage of forest as a proportion of the total area of the country from 67 percent to 17 percent.

18.15   69.   The course of average global temperature during the past 150,000 years and 25,000 years into the future. The natural course of climate (dashed [color] line) would be declining temperatures leading to the next glacial maximum, about 23,000 years from now. With greenhouse warming, a continuing rise of temperature may lead to a "super-interglaciation" within the next several centuries. The temperature may then be warmer than during the last interglaciation and warmer than at any time in human history. The decline toward the next glaciation would thereby be delayed by a millennium or more.

18.16   70.   A computer simulation showing possible changes in summer (June, July, August) precipitation resulting from a doubling of atmospheric CO_2. Many of the areas of projected decreased precipitation (large parts of central North America, eastern and southern South America, Western Europe, Africa, the Middle East, and central Asia) are prime agricultural areas.

18.17 71. Acidity record from a Greenland ice core showing peaks in sulphuric-acid precipitation attributable to major volcanic eruptions. The largest acid peak dates to 1815-1816, the time of the huge Tambora eruption in the East Indies, which produced "the year without a summer" (1816), as the volcanic dust and gases in the stratosphere reduced northern hemisphere temperatures at least 0.7°C. Subsequent eruptions of Krakatau, Katmai, and Agung also produced detectable climatic effects of smaller magnitude.

C18.1 72. Measurements of oxygen isotopes in the sediments of a Swiss lake and an ice core from the Greenland Ice Sheet show an abrupt and rapid change of climate at the end of the last glaciation (arrows). The curves, which can be viewed as recording changes in temperature, show a sudden shift in colder climate followed by an abrupt return to warmer postglacial climate. Detailed studies of the ice core indicate that at the end of the Younger Dryas event average temperature in Greenland rose about 7°C in only 40 years.

C18.2 73. Distribution of ice sheets in the North Atlantic region and North American ice-margin lakes during the Younger Dryas event. Rapid drainage of large volumes of meltwater into the western North Atlantic cooled the ocean surface and reduced its salinity, shutting down the thermohaline conveyor system. Air passing over the cold North Atlantic brought colder conditions to northwestern Europe that led to the growth of glaciers and a major change in vegetation communities.

EARTH SCIENCE SUPPLEMENTARY SLIDE SET

This supplementary slide set contains 111 colour images, mostly photographs, taken from the text. The left-hand column indicates the number of the corresponding figure in the text.

Fig. #

I-4   1.   Siccar Point, Berwickshire, Scotland. The vertical layers of sedimentary rock on the right, originally horizontal, were lifted up into their vertical position. Erosion developed a new land surface that became the surface on which the now gently sloping layers of younger sediments were laid. The gently sloping layers, which are named the Old Red Sandstone, are 370 million years old. At this locality, in 1788, James Hutton first demonstrated that the cycle of deposition, uplift, and erosion is repeated again and again.

I-5   2.   Meteor Crater, near Flagstaff, Arizona. The crater was created by the impact of a meteorite about 50,000 years ago. It is 1.2 km in diameter and 200 m deep. Note the raised rim and the blanket of broken rock debris thrown out of the crater. Many impacts larger than the Meteor Crater event are believed to have occurred during the Earth's long history.

I-6   3.   This thin, dark layer of rock (marked by the coin) is rich in the rare chemical element iridium and looks out of place in the thick sequence of pale-colored limestones above and below. The iridium-rich layer, here seen in the Contessa Valley, Italy, has been identified at many places around the world and is believed to have formed as a result of a world-circling dust cloud formed by a great meteorite impact about 66 million years ago.

I-9   4.   The African Rift Valley extends from the Red Sea in the north to Malawi in the south. A gigantic rent in the Earth's surface, hundreds of kilometers wide, marks the place where convection currents deep inside the Earth are splitting Africa in two. This LANDSAT image is of the eastern side of the Rift Valley (green) in central Kenya. To the east (right) a high plateau (red) marks the eastern edge of the Rift Valley. The dark lines in the valley are elongate fractures in the Earth's outermost layer. The five round features in the valley are volcanoes formed as a result of lava rising up the fractures.

1.9   5.   A supernova.

1.15   6.   Europa, smallest of the four large moons of Jupiter. Europa has a low density, indicating it contains a substantial amount of ice. The surface is mantled by ice to a depth of 100 km. The fractures indicate that some internal process must be disturbing and renewing the surface of Europa. The dark material (here appearing red) in the fractures apparently rises up from below. The cause of the fracturing is not known. The image was taken by *Voyager 2* in July 1979.

2.12A,B 7. A period of the active Sun. A. A vast, fiery prominence of hot gas bursting out from the photosphere through the chromosphere and corona. B. A huge sunspot with an unusual spiral structure breaks through the photosphere in 1982.

3.11 8. When a magnitude 6.8 earthquake struck Armenia on December 7, 1988, poorly constructed buildings with inadequate foundations collapsed like houses of cards. The principal cause of collapse was ground motion.

3.12 9. Gaping fissures in a residential area of Anchorage, Alaska, formed during the 1964 earthquake. The fissures result from liquefaction and failure of weak subsurface rocks.

4.7 10. The two most common minerals in the Earth's crust. Crystals of feldspar (green) and quartz (gray) from Pikes Peak, Colorado. This specimen is about 20 cm across.

C4.1 11. Because these two crystals are both quartz, they have the same crystal form. Although the sizes of the individual faces differ markedly between the two crystals, each numbered face on one crystal is parallel to an equivalent face on the other crystal. It is a fundamental property of crystals that, as a result of the internal crystal structure, the angles between adjacent faces are identical for all crystals of the same mineral.

C4.3 12. Distinctive external shape of pyrite FeS_2. The characteristic shape of pyrite is crystals with faces at right angles and with pronounced striations on the faces. The largest crystals in the photograph are 3 cm on an edge. The specimen is from Bingham Canyon, Utah.

C4.4 13. Some minerals have distinctive growth habits, even though they do not develop well-formed crystal faces. The mineral chrysotile sometimes grows as fine, cottonlike threads that can be separated and woven into fireproof fabric. When chrysotile is used for this purpose, it is referred to as asbestos.

C4.5 14. Relation between crystal structure and cleavage. Halite, NaCl, has well-defined cleavage planes; it always breaks into fragments bounded by perpendicular faces.

C4.6 15. Perfect cleavage of mica (variety muscovite) is illustrated by the planar flakes into which this specimen is being split. The cleavage flakes suggest leaves of a book, a resemblance embodied in the term *books of mica*.

C4.7 16. Color contrast between hematite and a hematite streak. Massive hematite is opaque, has a metallic luster, and appears black. On a porcelain plate, however, this mineral gives a red streak.

4.9A-D 17. Polished surfaces and thin slices reveal textures and mineral assemblages to great advantage. The specimen here is an igneous rock containing quartz (Q), feldspar (F), amphibole (A), mica (M), and magnetite (Mg). A. A thin slice mounted on glass. The slice is 0.03 mm thick, and light can pass through the minerals. B. A polished surface. The dashed rectangle indicates the area used to make the thin slice shown in part A. C. An area of the thin slice as viewed under a microscope. The magnification is 25x. D. The same view as in part C seen through polarizers in order to emphasize the shapes and orientations of individual grains.

5.2 18. An advancing tongue of basaltic lava setting fire to a house in Kalapana, Hawaii, during an eruption of Kilauea volcano in June 1989. Flames at the edge of the flow are due to burning lawn grass.

5.3 19. Lava flow rate is controlled by viscosity which in turn is controlled by temperature. The formation on which the geologist is standing, is pahoehoe lava formed from a very hot, low-viscosity, and therefore fast moving lava that was erupted in 1959. The upper flow (the one being sampled), which is relatively cool and therefore very viscous and slow moving, is an aa lava erupted from Kilauea volcano in 1989. They have the same basaltic composition.

5.4 20. Fountaining starts an eruption of Krafla, a basaltic volcano in Iceland. Use of a telephoto lens foreshortens the field of view. The geologist in a protective suit is making measurements several hundred meters away from the fountain.

5.5 21. This stream of low-viscosity (and therefore very hot) basaltic lava moving smoothly away from an eruptive vent demonstrates how fluid and free flowing lava can be. The temperature of the lava is about $1100\,^{\circ}C$. The eruption occurred in Hawaii in 1983.

5.6A-C 22. Tephra. A. Large spindle-shaped pyroclasts up to 50 cm in length cover the surface of a tephra cone on Haleakala volcano, Maui. B. Intermediate-sized tephra called lapilli cover the Kau Desert, Hawaii. The coin is about 1 cm in diameter. C. Volcanic ash, the smallest-sized tephra, covers leaves in a garden in Anchorage, Alaska, following the eruption of Mount Spurr.

5.8   23.   Mauna Kea, a 4200-m-high shield volcano on Hawaii, as seen from Mauna Loa. Note the gentle slopes formed by highly fluid basaltic lava. The view is almost directly north. A pahoehoe flow is in the foreground on the northeast flank of Mauna Loa.

5.9B   24.   Tephra cone in Arizona built from lapilli-sized basaltic tephra.

5.11   25.   Crater Lake, Oregon, occupies a caldera 8 km in diameter that crowns the summit of a once lofty stratovolcano, posthumously called Mount Mazama. Wizard Island is a small tephra cone that formed after the collapse that created the caldera.

5.14   26.   Shiprock, New Mexico. A. The conical tephra cone that once surrounded this volcanic neck has been removed by erosion. B. Diagram of the way the original volcano may have appeared prior to erosion.

5.16B 27.   Fractional crystallization. Layers of plagioclase (light gray) and chromite (black) formed by fractional crystallization in the Bushveld Igneous Complex, South Africa.

C5.1A-D 28.   Different textures in igneous rock. A. Obsidian, a wholly glassy igneous rock (extrusive). B. Basalt, a fine-grained igneous rock (extrusive). C. Gabbro, a coarse-grained igneous rock (intrusive). D. Basalt porphyry (extrusive). Sample A has the composition of a rhyolite, but B, C, and D have the same mineral assemblage—feldspar (white), pyroxene (dark green to black), and olivine (pale brown).

C5.2   29.   Three coarse-grained igneous rocks. Note the change in color from granite (left), which is light colored because it is rich in feldspar and quartz, through diorite (center), to gabbro (right), which is quartz-free and rich in pyroxene and olivine and therefore darker in color. Each specimen is 7 cm across.

C5.3A,B 30.   Two ways of forming a pyroclastic rock. A. Rhyolite tuff, formed by cementation of lapilli and ash, from Clark County, Nevada. B. Welded tuff from the Jemez Mountains, New Mexico. The dark patches are glassy fragments flattened during welding. Note the fragments of other rocks in the specimen. Both samples are 4 cm across.

Chap. 6 Opener 31. The Americas and the adjacent oceans. Yellow bands are mid-ocean ridges. Shape of the eastern coasts of North and South America were determined by the breakup of a giant continent (Pangea) about 200 million years ago. The line along which Africa and Europe broke apart from the Americas is the Mid-Atlantic Ridge. After breakup, the Americas moved west, Europe and Africa moved east.

7.6 32. Varves deposited in a glacial age lake in southern Connecticut. Each pair of layers in a sequence of varves represents an annual deposit. Light-colored silty layers were deposited in summer, and the dark-colored clayey layers accumulated in winter.

7.7 33. Ancient cross-bedded sand dunes that have been converted to sedimentary rock that crops out near Kanab, Utah. The inclination of the cross beds shows that the ancient prevailing winds were blowing from left to right.

7.11A,B 34. Comparison of textures developed in rocks of the same composition under uniform and differential stress. A. Granite, consisting of quartz, feldspar, and mica (the dark mineral) that crystallized under a uniform stress. Note that mica grains are randomly oriented. B. High-grade metamorphic rock, also consisting of quartz, feldspar, and mica, that crystallized under a differential stress. Mica grains are parallel, giving the rock a distinct foliation.

C7.3A-D 35. Progressive metamorphism of shale and the development of foliation. A. Slate from Bangor, Pennsylvania. Individual mineral grains are too small to be visible. Slaty cleavage records the beginning of metamorphism. B. Phyllite from Woodbridge, Connecticut. Mineral grains are just visible. Foliation is more pronounced. C. Schist, from Manhattan, New York. Mineral grains are now easily visible and foliation is pronounced. D. Gneiss, from Uxbridge, Massachusetts. Quartz and feldspar layers (light) are segregated from mica-rich layers (dark). Foliation is pronounced.

C7.5A,B 36. Texture of nonfoliated metamorphic rocks seen in thin section and viewed in polarized light. Notice the interlocking grain structure produced by recrystallization during metamorphism. Each specimen is 2 cm across. A. Marble, composed entirely of calcite. All vestiges of sedimentary structure have disappeared. B. Quartzite. Arrows point to faint traces of the original rounded quartz grains in some of the grains.

C8.2A   37.   A slice through a living coral from the Galapagos islands shows the annual layering (alternating dark and light bands rising from bottom to top of the section) of the calcium-carbonate skeleton. This layering preserves a record of changing surface water conditions, and therefore, of El Niño events.

8.19   38.   Waves arriving obliquely along a coast near Oceanside, California, change orientation as they encounter the bottom and begin to slow down. As a result, each wave front is refracted so that it more closely parallels the bottom contours. The arriving waves develop a longshore current that moves from left to right in this view.

8.27A   39.   Coastal emergence of eastern New Guinea. The emergent coast of the Huon Peninsula in eastern Papua New Guinea is flanked by a series of ancient coral reefs that form flat terracelike benches parallel to the shoreline. Each reef formed at sea level and was subsequently uplifted along this active plate margin. The highest reefs lie several hundred meters above sea level and are hundreds of thousands of years old.

9.1   40.   Maroon Creek, in Colorado's White River National Forest, produces a succession of small rapids where it flows over and between boulders scattered along its gravelly channel.

9.4   41.   A meandering stream near Phnom Penh, Cambodia. Light-colored point bars, composed of gravelly alluvium, lie opposite step banks on the outside of meander bends. Two oxbow lakes, the product of past meander cutoffs, lie adjacent to the present channel.

9.7   42.   The shifting channels of Rakaia River, flowing from glaciers in New Zealand's Southern Alps, form a braided pattern that is constantly changing form.

9.8   43.   Intricate braided pattern of the Brahmaputra River where it flows out of the Himalaya en route to the Indian Ocean. Noted for its huge sediment load, the river is as wide as 8 km during the rainy monsoon season.

9.14A,B   44.   A pair of satellite images shows the region where the Missouri River joins the Mississippi River near St. Louis, Missouri A. In a typical summer (July 1988) and B. during the disastrous flood of July 1993 when weeks of torrential rains caused the streams of overflow protective levees and inundate numerous towns and vast areas of farmland. Losses, amounting to billions of dollars, included destroyed crops, closure of water treatment plants, severely damaged roads and bridges, and the destruction of entire communities.

9.15A,B   45.   Features attributable to catastrophic flooding in the Columbia Plateau region. A. Huge ripple marks formed by raging floodwaters as they swept around a bend of the Columbia River. Composed of coarse gravel, the ripples are up to several meters high, and their crests are us much as 100 m apart. B. Large boulder transported and deposited by floodwaters beyond the mouth of Grand Coulee, a major channel excavated by successive floods.

9.26   46.   The Leaning Tower of Pisa, Italy, the tilting of which accelerated as groundwater was withdrawn from aquifers to supply the growing city.

10.1   47.   A map of average snow cover in the northern hemisphere (expressed as percentage of land area covered by snow) during December, 1992 is based on data received from a microwave sensor aboard an orbiting satellite. Greatest snow cover lies in regions of continental climate in middle to high latitudes (northern North America and northeastern Asia) and high-altitude regions such as the Tibetan Plateau of central Asia.

10.2   48.   The lower limit of snow in late spring forms an irregular line across the flank of Mount Cook, the highest peak in New Zealand's Southern Alps. As the weather warms and the snow melts, the snow limit rises to its highest level at the end of the summer. This late-summer limit marks the annual snowline. Above the snowline, most of the ground remains snow-covered all year.

10.5A-C   49.   A. A small cirque glacier below a mountain summit in Alaska's Denali National Park. B. Dark bands of rock debris delineate the boundaries between adjacent tributary ice streams that merged to form Kaskawulsh Glacier, a large valley glacier in Yukon Territory, Canada. C. Several ice caps cover areas of high land on Iceland. Vatnaj okull, in the southeastern part of the island, is the largest ice cap (8300 km^2) and overlies an active volcano.

10.6   50.   A vertical satellite view of the valley-glacier complex that covers much of Denali National Park in south-central Alaska. Mount McKinley, the highest peak in North America, lies near the center of the glacier-covered region.

10.7   51.   Satellite view of Antarctica. The East Antarctic Ice Sheet overlies the continent, while the much smaller West Antarctic Ice Sheet covers a volcanic island arc and surrounding seafloor. Major ice shelves occupy large coastal embayments. The ice-covered regions of Antarctica nearly equal the combined areas of Canada and the coterminous United States.

10.17 52. Contorted medial moraines of Susitna Glacier in the Alaskan Range provide striking evidence of periodic surges during which tributary ice streams advance at rates far greater than those of adjacent nonsurging glaciers.

C10.1 53. A vast sheet of rocky debris covers the lower ablation zone of Sherman Glacier following the collapse of a large mountain buttress during the 1964 Alaska earthquake. The debris cover impeded melting, leading to a negative mass balance and a subsequent advance of the glacier terminus.

11.1 54. Because marble is composed of soluble calcite, this marble tombstone standing in a New England cemetery since the early nineteenth century shows the corrosive effects of the carbonic acid present in rainwater. Over the years the rock surface has been slowly dissolved making the once sharply chiseled inscription illegible.

11.3A 55. This granite outcrop in Yosemite National Park, California, displays sheetlike joints, giving a stepped appearance to the mountain slope. The jointing is thought to result from progressive removal of overlying rock, leading to reduced pressure. This causes expansion of the uppermost rock, which fractures along planes parallel to the land surface.

11.3B 56. Granite on the side of Gondola Ridge in Antarctica is so intensely weathered that it resembles Swiss cheese. Such cavernous weathering is produced by crystallization of salt in small cavities and along grain boundaries.

11.6 57. Widespread deforestation in Rondonia, Brazil has devastated a formerly luxuriant rain forest and led to accelerated runoff and erosion. Soils on this landscape quickly lose their natural fertility when forest is converted to crops or grazing land, leaving a degraded landscape with little value.

11.11 58. A satellite image of the region near Harrisburg, Pennsylvania, reveals a complicated series of northeast-trending ridges and valley produced by differential erosion of sedimentary rocks. Ridges are underlain by resistant sandstones and conglomerates, while valleys are underlain by more-erodible shales. The folded structure of the rocks is clearly visible due to the pronounced topographic relief between the less-erodible and more-erodible strata.

11.13 59. Alluvial terraces adjacent to Cave Stream, South Island, New Zealand, record former floodplains that were abandoned when the stream incised its channel and reached a new level.

11.14 60. A symmetrical alluvial fan has formed at the margin of Death Valley, California, where a stream channel emerges from a steep mountain canyon.

11.15 61. Delta of Nile River, along the Mediterranean coast of Egypt. The reddish color in this vertical satellite image denotes vegetation growing on the fertile delta sediments. The delta and Nile River are bounded by a desert landscape of bare rock and shifting sands.

11.17 62. Most of a city block in Winter Park, Florida disappeared into a widening crater as this sinkhole formed in underlying carbonate bedrock.

11.18 63. Steep limestone pinnacles up to 200 m high, surrounded by flat expanses of alluvium, form a spectacular karst landscape around the Li River near Guilin, China.

11.19 64. A deglaciated bedrock surface beyond Findelen Glacier in the Swiss Alps displays grooves and striations etched by rocky debris in the base of the moving glacier when it overlay this site. In the background rises the Matterhorn, a glacial horn sculpted by glaciers that surround its flanks.

11.20A,B 65. Typical landforms of glaciated mountains. A. This cirque, carved in sedimentary rocks of the Brooks Range, in northern Alaska, was the site of a former glacier that built the large bouldry end moraine on the floor of the cirque. B. A deep U-shaped valley in the southern Coast Range of British Columbia, Canada, was carved during repeated invasions of ice-age glaciers that left the valley walls smoothed and abraded to a height of nearly 2 km above the valley floor.

11.21 66. Trekkers atop the Pulpit, a spectacular vantage point far above Lysefjord, can look far inland toward the source region of the glacier that carved this fjord, typical of numerous others that indent the rocky western coast of Norway.

11.22 67. A field of drumlins in Dodge County, Wisconsin, each shaped like the inverted hull of a ship, are aligned parallel to the flow direction of the continental ice sheet that shaped them during the last glaciation.

11.23 68. Lobuche Glacier, which flows out of a high cirque near Mount Everest in the

Himalaya, has retreated upslope from a terminal moraine it deposited on the margin of Khumba valley during the nineteenth century.

11.24 69. Lake-filled kettles are scattered over the surface of an end-moraine complex in the lake district of central Chile that formed at the end of the last glaciation when debris-covered stagnant ice slowly melted away.

11.25 70. Coalescing barchan dunes migrate slowly across a vast plain in the Namibian Desert of southwest Africa. The steep slopes of the dunes descend in the direction toward which the prevailing wind blows and show that the dunes are moving in the direction of the photographer.

11.27 71. A steep cliff of loess rises above a road near Xi'an on the Loess Plateau of central China. The bulk of this loess accumulated during the last glacial age when cold, dry winds blowing across desert basins of central Asia swept up fine dust, transported it eastward, and deposited it like a thick blanket across the landscape. The reddish-brown band near the base of the exposure is an ancient soil that formed during an interval of moist, warm climate.

11.28 72. A sandy beach along the shore of Bora Bora, a volcanic island in French Polynesia, consists of coral and shell debris carried landward by wave action and mixed with lava fragments from the eroding volcano.

11.29A,B 73. Coastal landforms. A. The long, curved spit of Cape Cod, Massachusetts, has been built by longshore currents that rework glacial deposits forming the peninsula southeast of Cape Cod Bay. B. Barrier islands off Corpus Christi, Texas (along south side of large bay) seen from an orbiting satellite. To the right is the Gulf of Mexico. Padre Island National Seashore occupies the barrier island extending south from Corpus Christi Bay.

12.8 74. Puy-en-Velay, one of the many ancient volcanic rocks in France. It was on such a puy that Blaise Pascal arranged for rock climbers to carry out the experiment proving that air pressure decreases with altitude.

12.20A-C 75. Principal types of clouds I. A. Cumulus B. Cumulonimbus. Note the plume spreading sideways. C. Altocumulus

12.20D-F 76. Principal types of clouds II. A. Cirrostratus B. Stratocumulus C. Stratus

12.20G-I 77. Principal types of clouds III. A. Altostratus B. Nimbostratus C. Cirrus

76

13.8   78. A low pressure center (cyclone) centered over Ireland and moving eastward over Europe. The counterclockwise winds of a northern hemisphere low are clearly shown by the spiral cloud pattern.

13.20   79. A thunderstorm over Tucson, Arizona. Note the dark cumulonimbus clouds, the dense rain and the lightning in the clouds.

13.22   80. A tornado crossing the plains of North Dakota.

13.23   81. Hurricane Andrew, one of the largest and strongest hurricanes in modern times, spawned over the Atlantic Ocean and slammed into Florida in August 1992. The hurricane, here photographed from above, packed winds in excess of 200 km/h.

14.4   82. In the late nineteenth century, Findelen Glacier in the Swiss Alps covered all the bare, rocky terrain seen here in the lower part of its valley. Since that time, the glacier terminus has retreated far upvalley in response to a general warming of the climate.

14.11   83. Horizontal benches at several levels above the surface of Great Salt Lake, Utah, mark shorelines of Lake Bonneville, a vast Pleistocene lake. At its maximum extent and depth during the last glaciation, the surface of Lake Bonneville stood more than 300 m above that of the present lake.

14.24   84. The explosive eruption of Mount St. Helens in 1980 produced a rapidly rising column of ash and gas that reached the stratosphere. There, upper-level winds transported the eruptive products eastward across the United States, and eventually around the world. Although the climatic effects of the relatively modest eruption were unimpressive, much larger explosive eruptions during the last 200 years have cooled temperatures in the northern hemisphere by 0.3 to 0.7°C.

15.4A,B   85. The Indiana Dunes. A. Pioneer species start the process of building an ecosystem on a dune. B. The climax community of a dune.

15.5A,B   86. Extrinsic events can greatly change an ecosystem. A. Yellowstone National Park after the great fire of 1988. B. Vegetation re-establishing itself. Yellowstone National Park two years after the great fire.

15.11   87. The Great Barrier Reef on the continental shelf of northeastern Australia is one of the world's most diverse marine ecosystems.

15.12A-D 88. So-called anteaters (usually they eat termites) from different parts of the world are different species; they fill the same niches but are not competitive because they do not come in contact. A. Short-beaked echidna (Australia) B. Tamandua (Central America) C. Pangolin (Malaysia) D. Giant anteater (Venezuela)

15.14 89. Acanthodian fish were the first animals to develop jaws. The fossil acanthodian (Cheiracanthus murchisoni), found in Devonian aged rocks in Banffshire, Scotland, lived about 400 million years ago. The lower jaw is visible at the lower right-hand edge of the specimen. The fossil is about 5 cm long.

15.16 90. Gasosaurus, one of huge flesh-eating Jurassic dinosaurs. Gasosaurus was up to 2 m high and 4 m long. Mammals that lived at the same time as Gasosaurus were small, about the size of mice or rabbits, and probably of little interest to the large dinosaur.

15.18 91. The extraordinary ecosystem around a black smoker at a depth of 2500 m in the Pacific Ocean. Bacteria that derive their energy inorganically through the oxidation of H_2S brought up by the smoker are the autotrophs. The heterotrophs that live directly or indirectly on the autotrophs include worms, clams, starfish, crabs, and skates.

15.19 92. Erosion as a result of overgrazing and poor farming practice in Ethiopia.

15.20 93. Algal bloom due to eutrophication on a pond in western New Jersey.

16.6A,B 94. A. Procaryotic cell. A bacterial cell devoid of visible organelles and with the DNA concentrated in a poorly defined nucleoid that is not separated from the cytoplasm by a membrane. B. Eucaryotic cell from a plant root with a well-defined, membrane-bound nucleus and varied cytoplasmic organelles. Note that the cells are colored because they have been stained.

16.7 95. Examples of the most ancient fossil procaryotes ever found. 3.5 billion-year old microfossils in chert from Western Australia. Adjacent to each photograph is a sketch. Magnification is indicated by the scale.

16.8A,B 96. Evidence of the antiquity of life. Stromatolites are layered growths that form in warm, shallow seas when photosynthetic bacteria cause dissolved salts to precipitate. A. Fossil stromatolites greater than 1.5 billion years old from the northern Flinders Range, South Australia. B. Modern stromatolites forming in the intertidal zone, Shark's Bay, Western Australia.

16.10   97.   Banded-iron formation of the Hamersley Range, Western Australia, formed during the Lower Proterozoic Eon. Banded-iron formations are chemical sediments and are thought to have formed when iron in solution in seawater was precipitated as a result of photosynthetic bacteria releasing oxygen. The woman in the foreground is Dr. Janet Watson, a distinguished English geologist.

C16.2   98.   Root nodules on white clover produced by colonies of nitrogen-fixing bacteria.

16.12A,B   99.   Two members of the Ediacara fauna from South Australia. These are the most ancient multi-celled animals that have ever been found. A. *Mawsonia spriggi*, a discoid shape, possibly a floating animal like a jellyfish. B. *Dickinsonia costata*, a curious worm-like creature.

16.13   100.   Fossil trilobite from the Cambrian Period. Trilobites were one of the first animals to develop a hard, chitin covering, presumably as a defense against predators. This sample was collected in Utah.

16.16A,B   101.   Ferns and club mosses are modern representatives of the seedless plants that first established themselves on the land in the Silurian. A. Fossil fern about 350 million years old. B. *Thelypteris phegopteris*, a modern fern that is also known as the long beech fern, showing spores on the undersides of the frond.

16.17A,B   102.   Naked-seed plants developed from the seedless late in the Devonian Period. A. A leaf of *Glossopteris*, a family of seed-fern plants that spread through Southern Gondwana. B. Leaves of modern fossil gingkos. The fossil is from North Dakota. Gingkos are long-lived relics of the ancient family of naked-seed plants.

16.19   103.   *Pikaia*, a soft-bodied animal from the Burgess Shale in British Columbia, is the earliest known chordate. *Pikaia* is the most ancient member of the group that became the vertebrates and to which we humans belong.

17.5   104.   A rich vein in Potosi, Bolivia, containing chalcopyrite, sphalerite, and galena cutting andesite. The andesite has been altered by the hydrothermal solution that deposited the ore minerals.

17.7A,B   105.   Sedimentary iron deposit of the Lake Superior type. A. Unaltered iron-rich sediments of the Brockman Iron Formation in Hamersley Range of Western Australia. The white layers are largely chert, whereas the darker bluish and reddish layers consist mainly of the iron-rich silicate, oxide, and carbonate minerals. The grade is about 25 percent iron. B. Altered iron-rich sediment from the same formation shown in A. Leaching of silica during weathering has formed a secondarily enriched mass of iron minerals that is rich enough to be an ore. The grade is about 60 percent iron.

17.8   106. Stratabound ore of lead and zinc from Kimberley, British Columbia. The layers of pyrite (yellow), sphalerite (brown), and galena (grey) are parallel to the layering of the sedimentary rock in which they occur. The specimen is 4 cm across.

17.10   107. Gold is recovered from fossil placers in Witwatersrand basin, South Africa. The gold is found at the base of conglomerate layers interbedded with finergrained sandstone, here seen in weathered outcrop at the site where gold was first discovered in 1786.

17.11A,B   108. Residual mineral deposits rich in iron and aluminum are typically formed under tropical or semitropical conditions. A. Red laterite enriched in iron, near Djenne, Mali. Laterites can sometimes be rich enough to be residual iron ores. Such ores have been mined in the past, but no large mining activity of residual iron ore is occurring today. B. Bauxite from Weipa in Queensland, Australia. Long-continued leaching of clastic sedimentary rocks under tropical conditions has removed most of the original constituents, such as silica, calcium, and magnesium, leaving a rich bauxite consisting largely of the mineral gibbsite ($Al(OH)_3$). Nodules of gibbsite form by repeated solution and redeposition. The Weipa bauxite deposits are among the largest and richest in the world.

18.3   109. Overgrazing during years of drought killed much of the vegetation in this part of the Sahel in Senegal. Without vegetation, topsoil is eroded and the land becomes infertile.

18.4   110. Barchan dunes advance from right to left across irrigated fields in the Danakil Depression, Egypt.

18.7   111. Vast bodies of carbonate rocks, like the Dolomites of northern Italy, constitute reservoirs of carbon dioxide that has been temporarily removed from the carbon cycle. Once exposed at the surface, carbonate rocks are weathered and eroded, thereby freeing CO_2, which reenters the carbon cycle.

AUDIO-VISUAL RESOURCES

AUDIO-VISUAL RESOURCES FOR TEACHING

In my opinion, a fundamental part of the teaching of Earth science should be to expose students to beautiful, moving, revealing, and instructive images of our planet—as many and as often as possible. In the Sample Course Syllabi I have suggested a number of good titles, and more are offered in this section.

There are so many good audio-visual resources available today on topics relevant to Earth science that it is impossible to summarize them concisely. Instead of providing a long list of distributors, I have chosen a sampling of titles from a few distributors that—in my own experience—consistently offer good service and a wide range of high quality audio-visual resources in Earth science and related fields. Some (but not all) of the titles are films, videos and slides that I have used successfully in my own classes.

For each reference given here, the name and address of the company is provided, along with a sampling of some of the available titles that might be useful in your Earth science courses. In most cases, the *title of the resource material* is shown in italics, whereas **names of distributors or manufacturers** are bolded.

SLIDE SETS

In addition to the slide sets listed below, two sets are available as a publisher's supplement to *The Blue Planet.* Refer to the section on **Supplements.**

The following three slide sets (and other slide sets, images, films, maps, and publications) are available from the Order Department, **Lunar and Planetary Institute,** 3303 NASA Road 1, Houston, TX 77058-4399 Tel: (713) 486-2172.

- *Shuttle Views the Earth: The Oceans from Space* Shuttle photographs of naturally-occurring sea surface features, as well as the meteorological and oceanic influences on land masses.
- *Shuttle Views the Earth: Clouds from Space* Some of the most informative and visually impressive cloud photographs. The unique perspective of Shuttle photography helps us to understand weather patterns and the development of weather systems worldwide.
- *Shuttle Views the Earth: Geology from Space* Shuttle photographs enable us to trace fault margins in the Earth's crust and observe large structures in their entirety and in the context of their surroundings. The images reveal how much of the Earth's surface is covered by vast deserts and provide comparisons of old volcanic structures with young erupting volcanoes.

The following slide sets (and others, as well as CD-Roms, software, and other educational tools) are available from **MMI Corporation,** 2950 Wyman Parkway, PO Box 19907, Baltimore, MD 21211 Tel: (410) 366-1222. Request both the Astronomy and Earth Science catalogues.

- *Visions of Spaceship Earth.*
- *Earth's Atmosphere.*
- *Weather: Cloud Formation, Storms and Related Phenomena.*
- *Weather: Fronts and Related Phenomena.*
- *Topography of the Earth.*
- *The Sun: Nuclear Fusion and Solar Radiation.*
- *The Planet Earth: Its Formation, Structure, and Plate Tectonics.*

The **National Oceanographic and Atmospheric Administration** offers some excellent slide sets at reasonable prices, with explanatory notes to accompany the slides. They are available from the World Data Center A, Boulder Centers, and the National Geophysical Data Center, NOAA, Code E/GC, 325 Broadway, Boulder, CO 80303. Examples of slide sets include:

- *Mount Pinatubo: The June 1991 Eruptions.*
- *Earthquake Damage—General.*
- *Landslides.*
- *Tsunamis—General.*

OVERHEAD TRANSPARENCIES

Overheads are available from a number of distributors and, of course, many of the figures from the text are available as a publisher's supplement to *The Blue Planet* (see section on **Supplements**). A distributor noted for high quality, scientifically accurate, graphically appealing transparency sets is:

- **TASA Graphic Arts, Inc.,** 15 Nexus Lane, Tijeras, NM 87059 Tel: (505) 281-9090. TASA also supplies CD-ROMs featuring the well-known style of Tasa graphics.

FILMS & VIDEOS

The following videos are available (among many other titles) from **MMI Corporation,** 2950 Wyman Parkway, PO Box 19907, Baltimore, MD 21211 Tel: (410) 366-1222. These are examples of "single-concept" videos. They are short (mostly 8 to 16 minutes) videos with NASA film footage complementing shots of experimental set-ups, models, etc., designed to illustrate individual concepts in a very concise manner.

- *Atmospheric Circulation* (16 minutes)
- *Weather Fronts and Precipitation* (9 minutes)
- *Ocean Circulation* (9½ minutes)
- *Development of Shorelines* (9½ minutes)
- *Rock Weathering* (8½ minutes)

A good source for current video titles is the *Annenberg/CPB Collection Science Series.* Most of these are individual programs which are also available as parts of longer series. Available from The **Annenberg/CPB Collection,** Dept. SB2, PO Box 2345, S. Burlington, VT 05407-2345 Tel: (800) LEARNER Fax: (802) 864-9846.

- *Only One Atmosphere* (from the series *Race to Save the Planet*)
- *Evolution Through Time* (from the series *Earth Revealed*)
- *Sedimentary Rocks: The Key to Past Environments* (from the series *Earth Revealed*)
- *Wind, Dust and Deserts* (from the series *Earth Revealed*)
- *The Climate Puzzle* (from the series *Planet Earth*)
- *Gifts from the Earth* (from the series *Planet Earth*)

Another good source for current films and videos on a range of environmental, geological, and ecological topics is **Films for the Humanities & Sciences,** PO Box 1051, Fort Erie, Ontario, L2A 5N8, Canada (or) PO Box 2053, Princeton, NJ 08543-2053. Ask for the Ecology, Environmental Science, and Geology listings. Following is a selection of interesting titles:

- *Hole in the Sky: The Ozone Layer* (52 minutes).
- *In the Path of a Killer Volcano* (1993) NOVA This film NEVER FAILS to impress both students and colleagues. It documents the adventures of USGS volcanologists at Mount Pinatubo in 1991. (60 minutes).
- *The Heat is On: The Effects of Global Warming* (26 minutes).
- *Tornado Alert: What You Need To Know* (28 minutes).
- *Treasures of Neptune: Klondike on the Ocean Floor* (26 minutes) Gold Award, Houston Film Festival.
- *Assessing Our Planet's Health: Lester Brown* (30 minutes)
- *The Ocean Sink* (26 minutes)
- *Preserving the Rain Forest* (24 minutes)
- *Drought and Flood: Two Faces of One Coin* (18 minutes)
- *Hurricane!* (60 minutes)

It may be worth going to a little extra effort to obtain some of the following new and/or unusual films from the **United States Geological Survey** (USGS) Library, MS 955, 345 Middlefield Road, Menlo Park, CA 94025-3591 Tel: (415) 329-5009. Interesting titles include:

- *The Walls Came Tumbling Down: Earthquakes of the Holy Land* (1992) Amos Nur. 56 minutes.
- *Anatomy of a Hurricane* (1994) USGS 5 minutes.
- *Oceanfloor Legacy: A Critical Juncture* (1991) USGS An Emmy award-winning film concerning old radioactive drums, new dredge spills, and the Golden Gate. 29 minutes.
- *The Future of Energy Gases* (1993) USGS 30 minutes.
- *Surviving the Big One* (1990) KCET-TV 58 minutes.
- *Hidden Fury: The New Madrid Earthquake Zone* (1993) USGS 27 minutes.
- *The Awesome Power* (1989) NOAA A film about flash flooding. 15 minutes.
- *Time-Lapse Observations of the Columbia Glacier, Alaska* (1980) USGS Seven years in the life of a glacier in 5 minutes.
- *When the Earth Quakes* (1990) National Geographic Television. A history of seismology, seismologists, and the earthquakes they study. 28 minutes.

LASERDISCS

- *Earth Science Laserdisc* includes over 4000 photographs and diagrams as well as 280 frames of maps with an indexed image directory. Available from **MMI Corporation,** 2950 Wyman Parkway, PO Box 19907, Baltimore, MD, 21211 Tel: (410) 366-1222. Also available, *Plate Tectonics Videodisc* consisting of two video programs and 400 photos and diagrams on the major aspects of global tectonics.

OTHER AV DISTRIBUTORS

Additional sources for slides, films, videos, and other audiovisuals are:

- **JLM Visuals,** 920 7th Ave., Grafton, WI 53024 Tel: (414) 377-7775.
- **Key Line Educational Materials,** PO Box 166, Cedarburg, WI 53012-0166 Tel: (414) 375-1999.
- **Mineral Information Center,** 1325 Massachusetts Ave NW, Room 550, Washington DC, 20005 Tel: (202) 737-1872.
- **National Audio-Visual Center,** Information Service EQ, Washington, DC 20409 Tel: (301) 763-1896.
- **National Geographic Society,** 17th and M Streets NW, Washington, DC 20036 Tel: (202) 857-7378.

- **National Wildlife Federation,** 1400 16th Street NW, Washington, DC 20036 Tel: (800) 432-6564.
- **PBS Video,** 1320 Braddock Place, Alexandria, VA 22314 Tel: (713) 739-5380.
- **Time-Life Video,** 1271 Avenue of the Americas, New York, NY 10020 Tel: (212) 484-5940.
- **Union of Concerned Scientists,** Publications Department, 26 Church St., Cambridge, MA, 02238 Tel: (617) 547-5552.
- **Ward's Multimedia,** 5100 West Henrietta Rd., PO Box 92912, Rochester, NY 14692 Tel: (800) 962-2660.

COMPUTER RESOURCES

GETTING STARTED

The teaching of Earth science is becoming more and more dependent on computer resources; this is a fact of life in the 1990s. Now is a good time to think about incorporating computer resources into your teaching, but it can be REALLY HARD to face getting started. Probably the single best way to begin exploring "what's out there" is to get yourself hooked up to the INTERNET. If you are affiliated with a college or university or other research institution, most likely you can get an INTERNET address by making one or two phone calls to the right person or department. If you can get your computer hard-wired into the network at your institution (rather than going through a modem connection), you will have more flexibility in terms of the scope of things you can accomplish (and it will probably cost less). You will also have the option of using various software packages that make the whole e-mail and computer network scene seem much more user-friendly.

A very useful book is *The Whole Internet,* by Ed Krol. The complete reference and address of the publisher are given in the section on **Additional Resources.** This book explains in detail how to get connected to the *World Wide Web* (also known as *WWW* or *W3*). *W3* is sort of like a personal guide, like an index of the vast array of resources available on the INTERNET. In particular, you should investigate the *W3 Virtual Library*. The *Virtual Library* is a very user-friendly, comprehensive directory of INTERNET resources. The easiest way to access *W3* and the *Virtual Library* is through *MOSAIC,* a hypertext-based software package operating in a *WINDOWS* environment. *MOSAIC* is specifically designed as graphical interface to provide easy access to *W3. MOSAIC* and the *Virtual Library* will allow you to cruise at will through the *World Wide Web,* and you will be amazed at what you find—there is a whole universe of resources and information on the INTERNET!

SOFTWARE

Here are just a few references for software that might prove useful to you and your students in Earth Sciences. Ideas for classroom and laboratory activities and assignments are suggested for some of these programs in the *Laboratory Manual for The Blue Planet,* by Marcia Bjørnerud, John M. Hughes, and A. Dwight Baldwin, Jr., available from the publisher. Some of this software is in the public domain (i.e., available free of charge), and some of it is under copyright.

▸ Alpha, Tau Rho (1989) *How to Construct Two Paper Models Showing the Effects of Glacial Ice on a Mountain Valley.* USGS Open File Report 89-640B (Macintosh with HyperCard 2.0).

▸ Alpha, Tau Rho (1993) *Landslide Effects.* USGS Open File Report 93-278B (Macintosh with HyperCard 2.0)

▸ Alpha, Tau Rho, and Gordon, Leslie (1991) *Make Your Own Model of a Volcano.* USGS Open File Report 91-115B (Macintosh with HyperCard 2.0).

▸ Alpha, Tau Rho, and Gordon, Leslie (1992) *Earthquake Effects.* USGS Open File Report 90-257B (Macintosh with HyperCard 2.0).

▸ Alpha, Tau Rho, Lahr, John C., and Wagner, Linda F. (1989) *Fault Motion, Loma Prieta, California Earthquake of October 17, 1989.* USGS Open File Report 89-640B (Macintosh).

▸ *Environmental Software Programs.* (IBM) Interactive educational software in the public domain ("shareware"), produced by the US Environmental Protection Agency (EPA) and Purdue University. Titles include *Surface Water Education System* (by D. Kim and B. Engel); *Wetlands Education System* (by D. Johannesen and J. Gurganus); *Groundwater Education System* (by B. Engel and J. Gurganus); and *Best Management Practices for Soil Erosion* (by L. Field, B. Engel, D. Jones, and M. Strickland). Available from The Farm Building Plan Service, **Purdue University,** 1146 AGEN Building, West Lafayette, IN 47907-1146 or from **Public Brand Software,** PO Box 51315, Indianapolis, IN 46251 Tel: (800) 426-3475 Fax: (317) 856-2086 or from **USEPA,** 77 W. Jackson, WCP-15J, Chicago, IL 60604-3590.

▸ *IRIS (Interactive River Simulation System).* An interactive program designed by Cornell University to simulate river systems. Used by the US Army Corps of Engineers, US Bureau of Reclamation, US Fish and Wildlife Service, and United Nations.

▸ *ORBITS: VOYAGE Through the Solar System.* An interactive hypermedia atlas of the Solar System for PCs. Available from **Software Marketing Corporation,** 9831 South 51st St., Bldg. C-113, Phoenix, AZ 85044 Tel: (602) 893-2400.

▸ *SIMEARTH.* A computer game based loosely on the Gaia Hypothesis. Available from **Maxis Corporation,** 1042 Country Club Dr., Suite C, Maraga, CA 94556 Tel: (415) 376-6434.

▸ *STELLA II.* Macintosh software to facilitate quantitative analysis of complex systems and cycles; first designed for studies of population dynamics in ecosystems, ideal for study of geochemical cycles. Available from **High Performance Systems, Inc.,** 45 Lyme Road, Suite 300, Hanover, NH 03755 Tel: (603) 643-9636 Fax: (603) 643-9502.

▸ *TIME MACHINE EARTH.* A PC-compatible program that displays plate reconstructions for user-specified times in the geologic past. Available from **Sageware Corporation,** 1282 Garner Ave., Schenectady, NY 12309 Tel: (518) 377-1052.

▸ *Water Budget.* Facilitates understanding of recharge, usage, deficit, and surplus in water budgets, with a built-in database from 45 locations worldwide. Available from **EME,** 41 Kenosia Ave., PO Box 2805, Danbury CT 06813-2805. Other software packages from EME include *Water Pollution, Hothouse Planet,* and *Our Ozone Crisis.*

▸ In addition to the above programs, spreadsheets are often useful for student exercises involving quantitative analysis and graphical representation of data. Commonly used spreadsheets include: *Excel* (PC and Macintosh), *Lotus 1-2-3* (PC), *Quattro Pro* (PC) and *WINGZ* (PC and Macintosh). These programs are widely available from software distributors. Instructions for beginners are provided in the Laboratory Manual.

NETWORK POSTINGS & ON-LINE DATABASES

A vast amount of material is available now on computerized networks and on-line databases, some free through networks like INTERNET, and others through commercial vendors. This is a sampling of the types of services you might find helpful in your teaching (and/or research):

▸ *AGRICOLA* is an on-line database containing about 3 million records on agriculture, pesticides, forestry, ecology, etc. Available through **CISTI** (Canadian Institute for Scientific and Technical Information), CAN/OLE Montreal Road, Ottawa, Ontario K1A 0S2 Canada Tel: (613) 993-1210.

▸ *Global Environmental Change Report* contains the full texts of scientific, legislative, and other articles and reports on global warming, ozone depletion, deforestation, etc. Available through **CompuServe.**

▸ The **International Geosphere-Biosphere Programme** has an electronic bulletin board on *OMNET,* called *IGBP.NEWS,* which contains information on meetings and contacts for the International Geosphere-Biosphere Programme. (The IGBP coordinates research on global change, with projects on terrestrial ecosystems, atmospheric chemistry, hydrological cycle, coastal zones, ocean fluxes, palaeoscience, land use/cover change, DIS, global biogeochemical modelling, and networks of regional research centres.) Send items for posting to *IGBP.Secretariat.*

▸ **National Geophysical Data Center (NGDC)** maintains an on-line database on

INTERNET called *GOLD* (for Geophysical On-Line Data). Much of the data comes from the observational programs of NOAA, and from cooperative arrangements with other government agencies, universities, and foreign organizations. The service includes data on seismology, geomagnetism, topography, global change, meteorology, paleoclimates and natural recorders of climate variability, ocean drilling, solar data, and more. The e-mail access address is: *ftp.ngdc.noaa.gov* or write to NOAA/NGDC, Mail Code E/GC, 325 Broadway, Boulder, CO 80303-3328 Tel: (303) 497-6826 Fax: (303) 497-6513.

▸ *Science and Technology Information System (STIS)* is an electronic information dissemination service that provides access (free) to National Science Foundation publications. STIS, National Science Foundation, Office of Information Systems, Room 401, 1800 G Street NW, Washington, DC 20550 Tel: (202) 357-7555 Fax: (202) 357-7663 E-mail: stis-request @nsf.gov (INTERNET) or stis-req@NSF (BITNET).

E-MAIL, MAILING LISTS & LOCAL BBSs

E-mail and local bulletin board systems are fast becoming a preferred way of communicating with students. They can be especially useful for very large classes, in which it may be impossible to maintain personal contact with each participant. A helpful reference is:

▸ *CABBS:* A Computer Accessed Bulletin Board Systems starter kit shows how to start your own local bulletin board system. Available from the **Corporation for Public Broadcasting Annenberg/CPB Collection,** Dept. SB2, 901 E Street NW Washington, DC 20004-2037.

There are also many (very many!) e-mail discussion groups and mailing lists that may be of interest to Earth scientists. They include, among many others:

▸ *AQUIFER* (listserv@ibacsata.earn) Covers pollution and groundwater recharge.
▸ *BIOSPHERE* (listserv%ubvms.bitnet@vm1.nodak.edu) Covers anything relating to the biosphere, including pollution, ecology, habitats, climate, etc.
▸ *CLIMLIST* (listserv@ohstvma.bitnet) Covers climatology and meteorology.
▸ *The Environmental Studies Discussion List* (listserv@brownvm.bitnet) Facilitates the exchange of information about Environmental Studies programs, including course design, student projects, information sources, etc.
▸ *ENERGY-L* (listserv@taunivm.bitnet) Covers energy-related topics.
▸ *ITRDBFOR* (listserv@asuacad.bitnet) Covers dendochronology.
▸ *PALAEOBOTANY* (listserv@vax.rhbnc.ac.uk) Covers palaeobotany.
▸ *QUAKE-L* (listserv@ndsuvm1.bitnet) Covers earthquakes.
▸ *TAXACOMA* (listserv@msu.bitnet) Systematic biology announcements.

CD-ROMs

▸ A CD-ROM is available as a publisher's supplement to *The Blue Planet.* It contains a compilation of photographs and line drawings from the Skinner & Porter texts.

▸ *GEOBASE* CD-ROM. An international bibliographic database covering physical and human geography, geology, and Earth, ecological, and developmental sciences. Available from **Elsevier/GeoAbstracts,** Regency House, 34 Duke St., Norwich NR3 3AP England.

▸ *Geodynamics Multimedia Database* CD-ROM. Containing data as well as mapping and display options for 89,000 earthquakes, 1500 volcanoes, topography, and coastlines, as well as lab activities and teacher's guide. Available from **EME,** 41 Kenosia Avenue, PO Box 2805, Danbury, CT 06813-2805 Tel: (800) 848-2050. EME also offers a Multimedia CD-ROM entitled *Focus on Environment.*

▸ *Geologic Hazards* CD-ROM. Volume 1: Earthquakes. Volume 2: Volcanoes and Other Phenomena. Available from **NOAA** at the World Data Center A, Boulder Centers, and the National Geophysical Data Center, code E/GC, 325 Broadway, Boulder, CO 80303.

▸ *Small Blue Planet—The Electronic Satellite Atlas* CD-ROM. Highly recommended. Available from **Now What Software,** San Francisco, CA 94115 Tel: (415) 885-1689.

▸ *The Theory of Plate Tectonics* CD-ROM. **TASA Graphic Arts Inc.,** 15 Nexus Lane, Tijeras, NM 87059 (505) 281-9090.

OTHER COMPUTER INFORMATION

Two additional sources for general information about software and other computer applications are:

▸ **Gibbs Associates,** Box 706, Boulder, CO 80306-0706 Tel/Fax: (303) 444-6032.

▸ **Marco Polo Software,** Suite 330, 11767 Katy Freeway, Houston, TX 77079-1716 Tel: (713) 293-7727 Fax: (713) 293-9662.

For information concerning INTERNET access, contact:

▸ **DDN Network Information Center,** SRI International, Room EJ291, 333 Ravenswood

Ave., Menlo Park, CA 94025 E-mail: SERVICE@SRI-NIC.ARPA (Subject: HELP)

▸ See also Krol, *The Whole Internet,* full reference given in section on **Additional Resources.**

For information concerning BITNET access, contact:

▸ **EDUCOM Networking Activities,** PO Box 364, Princeton, NJ 08540 Tel: (609) 734-1878
E-mail: LISTSERV@BITNIC.BITNIC (Send the message: GET BITNET USERHELP)

ADDITIONAL RESOURCES

Here is a hodge-podge of other resources that may prove useful in the teaching of Earth System Science courses.

DIRECTORIES & SOURCEBOOKS

▸ *Directory of Great Lakes Education Material* (1992) **International Joint Commission,** Great Lakes Regional Office, 100 Ouellette Avenue, Eighth Floor, Windsor, Ontario, Canada, N9A 6T3 (or) PO Box 32869, Detroit, MI 48232-2869. This directory contains information about all sorts of educational materials related to the Great Lakes.

▸ *Earth Science Education Resource Directory* **American Geological Institute Publications Center,** PO Box 205, Annapolis Junction, MD 20702 Tel: (301) 953-1744.

EDUCATIONAL PAMPHLETS

▸ NOAA and UCAR/OIES, *Reports to the Nation On Our Changing Planet,* a series of informative educational pamphlets produced jointly by the National Oceanic and Atmospheric Administration (NOAA) and Office for Interdisciplinary Earth Studies/University Corporation for Atmospheric Research (UCAR/OIES). So far three titles are available in the series: The Climate System, Our Ozone Shield, and El Niño. An instructional guide with reproducible black-and-white images is also available for the ozone volume. Available free from **OIES,** PO Box 3000, Boulder, CO 80307 Tel: (303) 497-1682 Fax: (303) 497-1679.

BOOKS & ARTICLES ON OTHER TOPICS

▸ Booth, Vernon (1993) *Communicating in Science.* 2nd Edition, Cambridge: Cambridge University Press. A guidebook for writing and presenting scientific papers.

▸ Guptil, Stephen C., and Starr, Lowell E. (1988) Making maps with computers. *American Scientist,* Vol. 76 (March-April), pp. 136-142.

▸ Heron, Duncan, ed. (1992) *Figuratively Speaking: Techniques for Preparing and Presenting a Slide Talk.* The American Association of Petroleum Geologists, Tulsa, Oklahoma 74101-0979, ISBN 0-89181-806-5. This is the AAPG's guide to producing a good slide show and talk. It is useful in the preparation of lectures, and you may want to introduce the book to students who have been assigned a class presentation or talk. The book also contains guidelines for the preparation of poster sessions.

▸ Jerrard, H.G., and McNeill, D.B. (1992) *A Dictionary of Scientific Units.* 6th ed. Chapman & Hall.

▸ Kovach, Warren L. (1992) Conversations in the ether: Earth science electronic discussion groups. *Geotimes* (July), pp. 21-22.

▸ Krol, Ed (1994) *The Whole Internet: User's Guide and Catalog.* O'Reilly & Associates, Inc., 103 Morris Street, Suite A, Sebastopol, CA 95472 Tel: (800) 998-9938 or (707) 829-0515 E-mail: nuts@ora.com or uunet!ora!nuts

▸ O'Connor, Maeve (1992) *Writing Successfully in Science.* Unwin Hyman Academic.

▸ Planetary Group, University of Santa Clara at Ames Research Center (1977) *Planetary Geology for Earth Science Instruction* National Aeronautics and Space Administration, Moffett Field, California, 94035. This book is pretty old and may be difficult to obtain, but it contains useful exercises and interesting suggestions for demonstrating things like the Coriolis effect and wind-generated landforms.

▸ Rittner, D. *Everyone's Guide to Environmental Information.* Peachpit Press. Discusses information available from online database services such as INTERNET, CompuServe, EcoNet, and others.

RADIO

▸ *Earth and Sky,* a radio series concerning astronomy and the workings of the Earth, broadcast in five 2-minute programs each week, on over 500 stations throughout the US and worldwide. Sponsored by the American Geophysical Union and National Science Foundation. (See *Earth in Space* for a complete listing of stations.)

JOURNALS, NEWSLETTERS & MAGAZINES

▸ *Earth,* with feature articles on plate tectonics and geologic events, published six times a year by **Kalmbach Publishing Co.,** 21027 Crossroads Circle, PO Box 1612, Waukesha, WI 53187 Tel: (414) 796-8776.

▸ *Earth in Space,* a highly readable, informative journal published nine times a year by the American Geophysical Union. It is not limited to articles involving spacecraft or satellite imaging of Earth, but includes anything of note in the study of the Earth system. Many articles are abstracted from *EOS,* the regular newletter of the AGU. Available for $10 per year from **American Geophysical Union,** 2000 Florida Avenue NW, Washington, DC 20009 Tel: (202)-462-6900.

▸ *Earthquakes and Volcanoes,* a bimonthly publication from the USGS. Available from the **US Government Printing Office (GPO),** Washington, DC 20402-9325 Tel: (202) 783-3238.

▸ *EarthQuest,* published quarterly by the Office for Interdisciplinary Earth Studies, **University Corporation for Atmospheric Research (UCAR),** PO Box 3000, Boulder, CO 80307-3000. This is a very informative newsletter about global change, which now comes with "Science Capsule" inserts prepared specifically for teaching purposes.

▸ *Geotimes,* a newsmagazine for geoscientists, published monthly. Especially helpful is the feature Geologic Phenomena, which is a summary of current and continuing volcanic and seismic activity. **American Geological Institute,** 4220 King St., Alexandria, VA 22302-1507.

▸ *Global Change Newsletter,* from the International Geosphere-Biosphere Programme: A Study of Global Change (IGBP) of the International Council of Scientific Unions (ICSU), published three times a year. Available free from **IGBP Secretariat,** The Royal Swedish Academy of Sciences, Box 50005, S-104 05 Stockholm, Sweden Tel: (+46-8) 16 64 48 Fax: (+46-8) 16 64 05.

▸ *Journal of Geological Education,* published by the **National Association of Geology Teachers (NAGT) Inc.,** PO Box 5443, Bellingham, WA 98227-5443. This journal is a never-ending gold mine of ideas and information concerning the teaching of Earth science.

▸ *SEAN (Scientific Event Alert Network) Bulletin,* a monthly newsletter with details about fireballs, volcanic activity, and seismic activity worldwide. Available from **American Geophysical Union,** Circulation Department, 2000 Florida Avenue NW, Washington, DC 20009 Tel: (202)-462-6900.

▸ *WOVO News,* quarterly newsletter of the **World Organization of Volcano Observatories.** Good, very current articles about active volcanoes around the world. Published by the Institut de Physique du Globe c/o Dario Tedesco, Managing Editor, Osservatorio Vesuviano, Via Manzoni 249, 80123 Napoli, Italy. (WOVO News was in financial straits as of their last issue; they may have had to suspend operations while seeking additional financial support.)

MAPS & POSTERS

▸ American Water Resources Association cartoon poster showing the many uses of water. Available from the **American Water Resources Association,** 5410 Grosvenor Lane, Suite 220, Bethesda, MD 20814-2192 Tel: (301) 493-8600 or from USGS Books and Open File Reports Section, Box 25425, Denver CO 80225-0425 Tel: (303) 236-7476.

▸ The **Astronomical Society of the Pacific** offers a variety of beautiful posters, as well as slide sets and other educational tools concerning the solar system. 390 Ashton Ave., San Francisco, CA 94112.

▸ *Bay Area Earthquakes* dramatically represents earthquakes in the San Francisco Bay area in a Landsat satellite image map with more than 12,000 epicenters plotted on it. Available from the **USGS Branch of Distribution,** Box 25286, Federal Center, Denver, CO 80225-0425.

▸ *Erwin Raisz Landform Maps of the US, Europe, Asia and Africa.* Distributed by **Raisz Landform Maps,** PO Box 773, Melrose, MA 02176 Tel: (800) 242-3199 Fax: (617) 662-2622.

▸ **Geological Survey of Canada** cartoon poster showing the contribution of geology to our daily lives; flip side provides trivia on various topics including the Arctic, technology, geological surveys, the environment, and energy. Available from Communications Office, Geological Survey of Canada, Room 244, 601 Booth St., Ottawa, Ontario K1A 0E8 Canada.

▸ Simkin, T., Tilling, R., Taggart, J., Jones, W., and Spall, H. (1989) *This Dynamic Planet: A world map of volcanoes, earthquakes and plate tectonics.* **USGS** and **Smithsonian Institution.**

▸ *World Ocean Floor Map.* **EME,** 41 Kenosia Avenue, PO Box 2805, Danbury, CT 06813-2805 Tel: (800) 848-2050. Also *Mid-Atlantic Ridge Wall Chart.*

▸ *World Total Oil and Gas Reserves* (1992) British Petroleum. Distributed by **AAPG** (American Association of Petroleum Geologists) Bookstore, PO Box 979, Tulsa, OK 74101.

▸ Local topographic maps can also be ordered from: **US Geological Survey,** Branch of Distribution, Box 25286, Denver Federal Center, Building 810, Denver, CO 80225 or from the **Geological Survey of Canada,** 601 Booth St., Ottawa, Ontario K1A 0E8 Canada Tel: (613) 996-3919 Fax: (613) 996-9990.

SAMPLES & EQUIPMENT

▸ **David New.** Meteorites and other unusual rock and mineral samples. PO Box 278, Anacortes, WA 98221 Tel/Fax: (206) 293-2255.

▸ **David Shannon Minerals.** 1727 W. Drake Circle, Mesa, AZ 85202 Tel: (602) 962-6485.

▸ **Geological Enterprises, Inc.** Fossils and visual aids concerning fossils. Box 996, Ardmore, OK 73402 Tel: (405) 223-8537 Fax: (405) 223-6965.

▸ **OMNI Resources.** Fossils, minerals, maps, books, hammers, etc. PO Box 2096, Burlington, NC 27216 Tel: (910) 227-8300 Fax: (800) 449-6664.

▸ **Ward's Scientific Establishment,** 1840 Mattawa Ave., Mississauga, Ontario L4X 1K1 Canada Tel: (905) 279-4482 or 5100 West Henrietta Rd., PO Box 92912, Rochester, NY 14692 Tel: (800) 962-2660.

Note that the questions included in this test bank are not research questions. In other words, it is possible to answer every test question strictly by referencing information contained in the book. Suggestions for research questions, which require further sources of information, are provided in the book itself at the end of each chapter. Most (but not all) of the test questions are also non-cumulative, i.e., they are based primarily on material presented within each individual chapter. The test bank is also available in computerized format. For each chapter in the book, including the Introduction, the following types of questions are provided:

MULTIPLE CHOICE QUESTIONS: Answers are indicated by "x".

Instructions to students: Please circle the letter corresponding to the best answer.

FILL-INS: Answers are given in parentheses below each question.

Instructions to students: Please fill in the blank space with the correct word or words.

DEFINITIONS: Brief definitions are provided after each term.

Instructions to students: Briefly define each of the following terms.

TRUE-FALSE QUESTIONS: Answers (T) or (F) are given at the end of each question.

Instructions to students: Please indicate T for a true statement or F for a false statement.

SHORT-ANSWER QUESTIONS: Answers are provided after each question.

Instructions to students: Please answer each question briefly in the space provided. Answers in point form are acceptable.

LONGER-ANSWER QUESTIONS, ESSAYS & CRITICAL THINKING QUESTIONS:
Answers are not provided for these questions (because each student will formulate his or her answer differently), but page numbers for text references are given at the end of each question.

Instructions to students: Please answer each question briefly in the space provided. Continue on back if necessary, but indicate clearly that you have done so.
(or)
Instructions to students: Please answer each question in the examination book provided for you. Clearly indicate the number of the question corresponding to each answer.

INTRODUCTION

I. Multiple Choice Questions

1. The irregular blanket of loose, uncemented rock particles that covers the solid Earth is referred to as

    a.   petrolith.
    b.   lithosphere.
    c.   tectonics.
x   d.   regolith.

2. Plate tectonics is

    a.   the slow lateral movement of segments of the Earth's hard, outermost shell as a result of conduction currents deep inside the Earth.
x   b.   the slow lateral movement of segments of the Earth's hard, outermost shell as a result of deep convection currents deep inside the Earth.
    c.   the principal mechanism of heat transfer from the inside of the Earth.
    d.   caused by the transfer of part of the Earth's rotational energy to the Earth's surface, in the form of tides.

3. The significance of iridium-rich clay layers is that

    a.   iridium is a very rare element in the platinum group, and it is therefore very valuable.
x   b.   the iridium may have been deposited as a result of meteorite impacts.
    c.   iridium is thought to have caused the mass extinction of species in which the dinosaurs died out.
    d.   there is a shortage of iridium in the world.

4. The human population of the world currently is increasing by about _____ people per year.

x   a.   95 million
    b.   5 million
    c.   5 percent
    d.   5.5 million

5.   The hydrosphere includes

     a.   oceans, lakes, streams, underground water, snow and ice, and water vapor in the atmosphere.

x   b.   oceans, lakes, streams, underground water, and snow and ice.

     c.   oceans, lakes, streams, and water vapor in the atmosphere.

     d.   clouds, rain, snow, ice, lakes, streams, and the oceans.

6.   James Hutton

     a.   is widely considered to be the father of modern geology.

     b.   was a physician.

     c.   proposed a counter-theory to catastrophism, which stated that "the present is the key to the past."

x   d.   All of the above are true.

7.   The principle of uniformitarianism says that

     a.   geological processes change very slowly over time.

     b.   human activity has a small but significant effect on some geological processes.

x   c.   the Earth processes we observe today have operated throughout much of geologic time.

     d.   the Earth is a closed system, and its resources are limited.

8.   The complex group of related processes by which rock is broken down and the products moved around is called

     a.   weathering.

x   b.   erosion.

     c.   plate tectonics.

     d.   uniformitarianism.

9.   The surface expression of convection currents inside the Earth is

     a.   the growth of mountains.

     b.   continental drift.

     c.   plate tectonics.

     d.   the formation of new oceans.

x   e.   All of the above are true.

10.   The principle of catastrophism states that

x   a.   all of the Earth's major features, such as mountains, valleys, and oceans, have been produced by a few great catastrophic events.
    b.   the Earth processes we observe today have operated throughout much of geologic time.
    c.   geologic events such as earthquakes, volcanic eruptions, and floods have catastrophic impacts on human activities and lives.
    d.   geologic events which happen suddenly and with catastrophic impacts are more important than the cumulative effects of small, continuous processes.

II.   Fill-Ins

1.   The concept that some events in Earth history are so huge that they cannot be explained by ordinary processes is referred to as _____ .

    (catastrophism)

2.   The amount of heat energy needed to raise the temperature of 1 gram of water by 1 degree Celsius is called a _____ .

    (calorie)

3.   The population of the world today is approximately _____ .

    (5.5 billion, at the beginning of 1994)

4.   Approximately _____ percent of the Sun's radiation that reaches the Earth is absorbed by the land, the sea, or the atmosphere, while the remaining _____ percent is simply reflected back into space.

    (70...30)

5.   There are three main mechanisms of heat transfer: _____ , _____ , and _____ .

    (radiation...conduction...convection)

6. The increase in temperature with depth inside the Earth is called the _____ .

   (geothermal gradient)

7. The Earth can be considered as a system of four vast, interdependent reservoirs: the _____ , the _____ , the _____ and the _____ .

   (solid Earth...atmosphere...hydrosphere...biosphere)

III. Definitions

1. atmosphere: the mixture of gases, predominantly nitrogen, oxygen, carbon dioxide, and water vapor that surrounds the Earth.

2. biosphere: the totality of the Earth's organisms and, in addition, organic matter that has not yet been completely decomposed.

3. calorie: the amount of heat energy needed to raise the temperature of 1 gram of water by 1 degree Celsius.

4. catastrophism: the concept that all of the Earth's major features, such as mountains, valleys, and oceans, have been produced by a few great catastrophic events.

5. conduction: the means by which heat is transmitted through solids without deforming the solid.

6. convection: the process by which hot, less dense materials rise upward, being replaced by cold, dense, downward-flowing material to create a convection current.

7. Earth system science: the science that studies the whole Earth as a system of many interacting parts and focuses on the changes within and between these parts.

8. erosion: the complex group of related processes by which rock is broken down physically and chemically and the products are moved.

9. geothermal gradient: the rate of increase of temperature downward in the Earth.

10. global change: the changes produced in the Earth system as a result of human activities.

11. hydrosphere: the totality of the Earth's water, including the oceans, lakes, streams, water underground, and all the snow and ice, including glaciers.

12. hypothesis: an unproved explanation for the way things happen.

13. joule: the work done when a force of 1 Newton acts over a distance of 1 meter.

14. law (scientific): a statement that some aspect of nature is always observed to happen in the same way and that no deviations have ever been seen.

15. plate tectonics: the special branch of tectonics that deals with the processes by which the lithosphere is moved laterally over the asthenosphere.

16. radiation: transmission of heat energy through the passage of electromagnetic waves.

17. regolith: the irregular blanket of loose, uncemented rock particles that covers the Earth.

18. rock: any naturally formed, firm, and coherent aggregate mass of mineral matter that constitutes part of a planet.

19. scientific method: the use of evidence that can be seen and tested by anyone who has the means to do so, consisting often of observation, formation of a hypotheses, testing of that hypothesis and formation of a theory, formation of a law, and continual reexamination.

20. theory: a hypothesis that has been examined and found to withstand numerous tests.

21. uniformitarianism, principle of: the same external and internal processes we recognize in action today have been operating unchanged, though at different rates, throughout most of Earth history.

22. watt: a unit of power at the rate of 1 joule per second.

IV. True-False Questions

1. The principle of uniformitarianism is applicable only to geology, not to other branches of science. (F)

2. The principle of uniformitarianism cannot account for rare, catastrophic events such as meteorite impacts. (F)

3. Rocks deep inside the Earth are so hot that it is possible for them to flow like sticky liquids. (T).

4. Volcanic eruptions are unrelated to the output of energy from the Sun. (T)

5. The Earth's external processes (weather, climate, and erosion) are driven primarily by energy from the Sun, with a small contribution from tides. (T)

6. Radiation is the process by which heat is transferred through solid rock, or any other solid body, without changing the shape of the solid. (F)

7. The process of flow in solid materials is not directly observable, because it only occurs deep within the Earth. (F)

8. Earth system science is primarily useful in the study of natural Earth systems; it is not well-suited for the study of human-induced changes to these systems. (F)

9. Global change refers to the changes produced in the Earth system as a result of human activities. (T)

10. Conduction is the most important process by which heat is transferred from the Earth's interior to its surface. (T)

V. Short-Answer Questions

1. Give an example of the application of the principle of uniformitarianism to a branch of science other than geology.

Answer: The principle of uniformitarianism can be applied to the study of stars. Although the life cycle of a single star is far too long to observe in entirety, the cycles of birth, growth and death of stars follow a predictable pattern, so astronomers can use observations of stars at different stages in their life cycles to draw conclusions about newly observed stars. (Other examples are also possible; this is the example cited in the text).

2. What are the three main sources of energy reaching the surface of the Earth?

Answer: (1) the Sun, (2) the interior of the Earth, and (3) gravitational attraction by the Moon and Sun (i.e., the tides).

3. What is the difference between a hypothesis and a theory?

Answer: A hypothesis is a suggested but unproved explanation for the way things happen. A theory is a hypothesis that has been examined according to the scientific method, and found to withstand numerous tests.

4. How was the principle of uniformitarianism originally used by geologists to deduce that the Earth is very old?

Answer: The principle of uniformitarianism states that the processes we observe today have been operating throughout much of Earth history. Geologists observed processes like the erosion of sediments and determined that it takes a very long time to erode a mountain range, transport the sediment, deposit thick sequences of mud or sand in the ocean, and then turn these sediments into rock. Comparing these observations to rock sequences created through the same processes of erosion and deposition, geologists concluded that it must have taken a very long time for these rock sequences to form, and that the cycle of erosion, deposition, and rock formation has been repeated many times in Earth history. Therefore the Earth must have a very long history.

VI. Longer-Answer Questions, Essays & Critical Thinking Questions

1. Summarize your understanding of the steps involved in the scientific method. (p. 4)

2. Describe the process by which heat is transferred from the interior of the Earth by means of convection. (p. 13)

3. Some events, like meteorite impacts or floods of great magnitude, are of such great magnitude that we describe them as "catastrophic." However, we don't necessarily need to invoke catastrophism in order to explain these events; the principle of uniformitarianism can account for infrequent, catastrophic events in Earth history. Discuss. (p. 9-10)

4. What are some of the ways in which human activities have begun to cause changes in the Earth system on a global scale? (p. 10-12)

5. Why is it important for the study of the Earth as a system to incorporate a range of specialized areas of scientific understanding? (p. 4)

6. A very wide range of time scales is involved in the flows of material from one reservoir to another in the Earth system. Discuss and give some examples to illustrate this point. (p. 7)

CHAPTER 1: Fellow Travellers in Space: Earth's Nearest Neighbors

---

I.   Multiple Choice Questions

1.   Ancient astronomers believed that the entire Universe revolved around the Earth. This is referred to as the _____ astronomical system.

x   a.   geocentric
      b.   heliocentric
      c.   egocentric
      d.   Copernican

2.   The law of gravitation states that

      a.   what goes up must come down.
      b.   once a body is moving it will stop or change direction only in response to another force.
x   c.   every body in the universe attracts every other body.
      d.   all falling bodies, regardless of their mass, fall with uniform acceleration.

3.   The chemical composition of the Earth's crust is

      a.   about the same as that of the Sun.
      b.   about the same as that of the mantle.
      c.   typical of the overall composition of the Earth.
x   d.   None of the above is true.

4.   Stars are masses of material of such enormous density

      a.   that nuclear fission occurs at their cores.
      b.   because they have iron-nickel cores.
x   c.   that nuclear fusion occurs at their cores.
      d.   None of the above is true.

5.   Our solar system formed approximately

       a.   15 billion years ago.
x   b.   4.6 billion years ago.
       c.   3.9 billion years ago.
       d.   4.0 billion years ago.

6. H_2O

       a.   only exists on the Earth.
       b.   exists on Mercury and Venus, but only in the form of water vapor in the atmosphere because these planets are much hotter than the Earth.
x   c.   exists on Mars but only in the form of ice, because Mars is too cold for liquid water to be present.
       d.   is a major component of the Earth's atmosphere.

7.   The planets

x   a.   formed from the same cloud of gas and dust as the Sun.
       b.   formed in different places in space and were drawn to the Sun by gravity.
       c.   formed at the same time as the Sun.
       d.   were ejected from the Sun as molten matter early in its history.

8.   The terrestrial planets, including the Moon, all have

x   a.   crusts, mantles, and cores.
       b.   strong magnetic fields.
       c.   atmospheres.
       d.   asthenospheres that are close to the surface of the planet.
       e.   All of the above are true.

9.   Iron meteorites are believed to be

       a.   fragments of larger bodies shattered by gigantic impacts early in the history of the solar system.
       b.   similar in composition to the cores of the Earth and other terrestrial planets.
       c.   remnants of compositionally layered asteroids.
x   d.   All of the above are true.

10. Kepler recognized that the shape of the planetary orbits is

      a.   circular.
      b.   eccentric.
      c.   irregular.
x   d.   elliptical.

11. Which of the inner four planets has retrograde motion (spins in the opposite direction to the others, when viewed from the north pole)?

      a.   Mercury
x   b.   Venus
      c.   Earth
      d.   Mars

12. The Earth's asthenosphere is

      a.   a hot, plastic, "weak" layer of rock.
      b.   just below the lithosphere.
      c.   the same composition as the mesosphere.
x   d.   All of the above are true.

13. The atmospheres of Jupiter and Saturn

x   a.   are so thick that we have never been able to see or probe the surfaces of these planets.
      b.   have changed substantially in composition since the formation of the planets early in solar system history.
      c.   are composed primarily of heavy gases.
      d.   hide rocky and metallic cores, much like those of the terrestrial planets only bigger.

14. The crust of the Earth is

      a.   roughly the same as the mantle in overall composition and density.
x   b.   very variable in composition.
      c.   essentially the same as that of the other terrestrial planets, in terms of overall composition, density, and thickness.
      d.   None of the above is true.

15. The only terrestrial planet that does not have an atmosphere is

    a. Mars
    b. Earth
    c. Venus
x   d. Mercury

16. Mercury and the Moon lack atmospheres because

    a. they never released gases from their interiors through volcanic activity.
x   b. they are too small.
    c. they are not dynamic planets like the Earth, Venus, and Mars.
    d. All of the above are true.

17. The terrestrial planets and the Moon

    a. all underwent a period of partial melting during the final phase of planetary accretion.
    b. all separated into layers of differing composition during a phase of partial melting.
    c. had similar geologic histories up to about 4 billion years ago, but have evolved along different paths since then.
x   d. All of the above are true.

18. The differences between continental crust and oceanic crust on the Earth

x   a. are part of the evidence that plate tectonics is an active process on the Earth.
    b. are similar to crustal differences observed on the other terrestrial planets.
    c. are part of the evidence that the Earth's core is more active than that of the other terrestrial planets.
    d. range up to 8 km in thickness from one place to another.

19. To date, no spacecraft have landed on

    a. Venus.
x   b. Mercury.
    c. Mars.
    d. the Moon.

20. One of the outer planets is much smaller and less dense than the others. It is

    a.   Neptune.
    b.   Uranus.
    c.   Saturn.
x   d.   Pluto.

II.   **Fill-Ins**

1. There are _____ planets in our solar system.

(nine)

2. The planets revolve around the Sun in _____-shaped orbits.

(elliptical)

3. All of the planets, with the exception of _____ , rotate around their axes in the same direction as they are revolving around the Sun.

(Venus)

4. The formation of the solar system was completed about _____ years ago.

(4.6 billion)

5. The planetary bodies formed in the solar nebula by a process known as _____ .

(planetary accretion)

6. At the center of each of the terrestrial planets is a core made primarily of _____ .

(iron) other correct answers are (metal) or (metallic iron) or (iron and nickel)

7. The cores of the jovian planets are inferred to be composed of _____ .

(rock) or (rocky material)

8. The outer planets, with the exception of _____ , are shrouded by thick atmospheres rich in hydrogen and helium.

    (Pluto)

9. The terrestrial planets are all characterized by an internal structure consisting of three main layers: a _____ , a _____ , and a _____ .

    (core...mantle...crust)

10. The discovery of the law of gravitation is attributed to _____ .

    (Sir Isaac Newton)

11. The Earth's lithosphere is made up of the _____ part of the crust and the _____ part of the mantle.

    (lower...upper) or (bottom...top)

III. Definitions

1. asthenosphere: the region of the mantle where rocks become ductile, have little strength, and are easily deformed; it lies at a depth of 100 to 350 km below the surface.

2. continental crust: the part of the Earth's crust that comprises the continents, which has an average thickness of 45 km.

3. core: the spherical mass, largely metallic iron, at the center of the Earth.

4. crust: the outermost and thinnest of the Earth's compositional layers, which consists of rocky matter that is less dense than the rocks of the mantle below.

5. geocentric: a universe in which a stationary Earth is at the center and everything else revolves around it.

6. gravitation, law of: every body in the universe attracts every other body.

7. heliocentric: a universe in which a stationary Sun is at the center and everything else revolves around it.

8.   inner core: the central, solid portion of the Earth's core.

9.   jovian planet: giant planets in the outer regions of the solar system that are characterized by great masses, low densities, and thick atmospheres consisting primarily of hydrogen and helium.

10. lithosphere: the outer 100 km of the solid Earth, where rocks are harder and more rigid than those in the plastic asthenosphere.

11. mantle: the thick shell of dense, rocky matter that surrounds the core.

12. mesosphere: one of the four thermal layers of the atmosphere, lying above the stratosphere.

13. oceanic crust: the crust beneath the oceans.

14. outer core: the outer portion of the Earth's core, which is molten.

15. planetary accretion: the process by which bits of condensed solid matter were gathered to form the planets.

16. solar nebula: a flattened rotating disc of gas and dust surrounding the Sun.

17. terrestrial planet: the innermost planets of the solar system (Mercury, Venus, Earth, and Mars), which have high densities and rocky compositions.

IV. True-False Questions

1.   The Sun is a star about 5 million years old. (F)

2.   The universe is at least twice and possibly three times as old as the Sun. (T)

3.   The revolutions and rotations of the Sun, planets, and moons are inherited from the rotation of the cosmic gas cloud from which the solar nebula formed. (T)

4.   The four innermost planets are called terrestrial planets because they all have the same chemical composition and density as the Earth. (F)

5.   All of the planets farther from the Sun than Mars are much larger than the terrestrial planets, and consist primarily of thick, gaseous atmospheres. (F)

6.   The planets closest to the Sun move faster than those far away. (T)

7.   The orbit of each planet is an ellipse with the Sun at one focus. (T)

8.   The rings of Saturn are composed primarily of individual particles of ice. (T)

9.   Saturn is the only planet we know of which has rings. (F)

10. The present distribution of the planets (inner, rock planets and outer, icy planets) reflects the temperature and compositional gradients within the solar nebula during the processes of condensation and planetary accretion. (T)

11. The bulk composition of Jupiter and Saturn is essentially the same as that of the solar nebula from which they formed. (T)

12. The Earth differs from the other terrestrial planets in that its asthenosphere is unusually thick and buried deep within the planet. (F)

13. Jupiter and Saturn probably contain rocky cores that may be as much as 20 times the mass of the Earth. (T)

14. The metallic cores of the terrestrial planets are all approximately the same size. (F)

15. The Earth is the only planet that has an asthenosphere. (F)

V.   Short-Answer Questions

1.   Draw a diagram illustrating Kepler's law of equal areas.

Answer: (See Figure 1.6 in the text.)

2.   What were the three laws of planetary motion discovered by Johannes Kepler, and what does each one state?

Answer: (1) The law of ellipses: The orbit of each planet is an ellipse with the Sun at one focus;
(2) The law of equal areas: A line drawn from a planet to the Sun sweeps out equal areas in equal times;
(3) The law of orbital harmony: For any planet, the square of the orbital period in years is proportional to the cube of the planet's average distance from the Sun.

3. What are the four terrestrial planets? Why are they called "terrestrial"?

Answer: Mercury, Venus, Earth, Mars
They are called "terrestrial" because they are similar to the Earth, in having relatively high overall densities, rocky compositions, and differentiated (layered) internal structures.

4. Why is it considered likely that a nearby supernova had something to do with the solar system's formation?

Answer: A supernova is the most likely source for the heavy elements present in the Sun and the rest of the solar system. (It is also possible that a supernova may have created the shock wave that initiated compression and collapse of the interstellar cloud of gas and dust, leading to the formation of the solar nebula. This is not covered in the text.)

5. How does the rotation of Venus differ from that of the other planets?

Answer: The other planets rotate about their axes in the same sense in which they revolve around the Sun (which is also the same direction as the Sun's own rotation about its axis). Venus, in contrast, rotates in the opposite direction about its axis (retrograde rotation), as though it had been turned upside down.

6. How do scientists explain the rarity of CO_2 in the Earth's atmosphere?

Answer: On the Earth, plants and microorganisms have enabled carbon dioxide and water to combine, through photosynthesis, to make organic matter and oxygen. The burial of organic matter in sediment in effect removes carbon dioxide from the atmosphere.

7. Make a neat, well-labelled diagram showing the internal structure (as we know it) of the Moon. Compositional and variations should be noted.

Answer: (See Figure 1.14B in the text.)

8. In what states of matter is hydrogen thought to exist in Jupiter and Saturn?

Answer: In their atmospheres, hydrogen occurs as a gas, but deep inside the planets where pressures are very great, hydrogen may exist in the form of molecular and metallic liquids, and possibly even as solid metallic hydrogen.

9. Make neat, well-labelled diagrams comparing the sizes of cores of the four terrestrial planets.

Answer: (See Figure 1.14A in the text.)

10. Make a neat, well-labelled diagram showing the probable interior structure of Jupiter.

Answer: (See Figure 1.16 in the text.)

11. Make a neat, well-labelled diagram showing the interior structure of the Earth, including the layers of differing composition and rock strength.

Answer: (See Figure 1.13 in the text.)

12. Why do the giant planets possess much more volatile and icy material and mass than do the terrestrial planets?

Answer: The giant (or jovian) planets formed in the outer parts of the solar nebula, where temperatures were very cold, and icy materials were condensing. The terrestrial planets formed in the inner part of the solar nebular, where temperatures were much higher, and more refractory, denser rocky and metallic materials were condensing.

VI. Longer-Answer Questions, Essays & Critical Thinking Questions

1. The three key factors controlling the evolution of a planet are (1) size, (2) distance from the Sun, and (3) the presence or absence of a biosphere. Discuss, using the examples of Earth and Venus for comparative purposes. (p. 35)

2. Our Sun is currently in a phase of its stellar evolution in which it is producing helium from hydrogen present in its core. All other, heavier elements can form only in the cores of stars more massive than our Sun, or during the process of a supernova. If this is true, then how is it possible that elements heavier than helium exist in the Sun and in other parts of our solar system? (p. 30-31)

3. Why is it important to begin a study of the Earth system with a comparison of the Earth with other planets in our solar system? (p. 20-21)

4. Briefly describe the processes of star formation and condensation of material in the solar nebula. (p. 30-33)

5. Why are there layers of differing rock strength and different physical state within the Earth? (p. 36)

6. Why is understanding a planet's interior helpful in understanding its surface features and processes? (p. 35-38)

7. How might we go about determining whether plate tectonics is (or has ever been) an active process on other planets? (p. 35-38)

8. Venus and Earth are about the same size and mass. Degassing volcanoes on each probably discharged abundantly both CO_2 and H_2O into their atmospheres. Why is CO_2 a major constituent of the atmosphere only on Venus? Why is H_2O not a major constituent of the atmosphere on either planet? (p. 35)

CHAPTER 2: The Sun, Giver of Life

I.   Multiple Choice Questions

1. The death of a small-mass star, 0.25 times the mass of our own Sun, is

    a.   much more common than the very dramatic supernova explosions that occur at the deaths of more massive stars.
    x   b.   not observable because these stars are very long-lived, and the universe is too young for any of them to have evolved off the main sequence.
    c.   similar to the death of a 1-S star.
    d.   the process whereby elements heavier than carbon are created.

2. Which of the following statements is false?

    a.   Our Sun is in its hydrogen burning stage of evolution.
    b.   The main sequence lifetime of our Sun will last at least 4 billion more years.
    x   c.   After our Sun has exhausted its nuclear "fuel," its outer layers will erupt explosively as a supernova.
    d.   The Sun has inherited virtually all elements with masses greater than helium from earlier generations of stars.

3. Stars are masses of material of such enormous density

    a. that nuclear fission occurs at their cores.
    b. because they have iron-nickel cores.
 x c. that nuclear fusion occurs at their cores.
    d. None of the above is true.

4. Convection is

 x a. a mode of heat transfer in which hot, less dense materials rise upwards and are replaced by cold, denser, downward-flowing materials.
    b. the main mechanism of heat transfer in the terrestrial planets.
    c. the end result of the absorption of incoming solar radiation by the Earth.
    d. All of the above are true.

5. The radius of the Sun is hard to determine accurately because

    a. the Sun is so far away.
    b. it is constantly changing.
    c. it is so enormous compared with other bodies in the solar system.
 x d. it is hard to define the outer edge of a ball of gas.

6. There are about _____ galaxies in the universe.

 x a. 100 billion (10^{11})
    b. 100 billion billion (10^{20})
    c. 1 billion (10^9)
    d. 100 million (10^8)

7. Because of its distance from the Sun, the Earth receives just the right amount of light and heat to support life, but _____ and _____ are too hot and dry for life to exist.

    a. the Moon and Mars
    b. Mars and Venus
 x c. Venus and Mercury
    d. the Moon and Mercury

8.   The death of a giant star, five times as massive as our own, occurs as a

      a.   quiet burning out and core contraction due to no more remaining nuclear fuel.
      b.   violent transition into a white dwarf.
      c.   transition to a red giant, and then a white dwarf.
x   d.   supernova explosion.

9.   Nuclear fusion

      a.   converts some of the mass of an atom into energy.
      b.   has only been achieved in an uncontrolled manner (in hydrogen bombs) on Earth.
      c.   represents a potentially limitless energy source for society, if it can be achieved under controlled conditions.
x   d.   All of the above are true.

10.   In order to calculate the Sun's luminosity, scientists must first

x   a.   measure the energy flux reaching the Earth from the Sun.
      b.   know the surface area of the Earth's sphere.
      c.   calculate what fraction of the Sun's luminosity is received by the Earth.
      d.   All of the above are true.

11.   The PP chain and the CNO chain

      a.   are the two main types of energy-producing fusion reactions in the Sun and most other stars.
      b.   both involve the fusion of hydrogen nuclei to form helium plus energy.
      c.   have the same net result, but different intermediate steps.
x   d.   All of the above are true.
      e.   None of the above is true.

12.   Earth receives a tiny fraction, only about one _____ of the Sun's total energy output.

      a.   half
      b.   2 thousandth
      c.   2 millionth
x   d.   2 billionth

13. Which of the following is not one of the three essential properties of electromagnetic waves?

    a.   wavelength
    b.   frequency
x   c.   radiation
    d.   speed

14. Gamma rays (γ) are

x   a.   a form of highly energetic, short-wavelength electromagnetic radiation.
    b.   similar to neutrinos, and together these two forms of radiation are responsible for the transfer of energy from the Sun to the Earth.
    c.   generated in the core of the Sun and then absorbed in the photosphere, which slows down the transfer of energy from the Sun.
    d.   produced by fission reactions in the core of the Sun.

15. A neutrino is

x   a.   an essentially massless particle that moves at the speed of light.
    b.   part of the basic internal structure of a hydrogen atom.
    c.   the major form in which solar electromagnetic radiation reaches the Earth.
    d.   a negatively charged electromagnetic particle.

16. Which of the following is not a stage in the life cycle of a 1-S star?

    a.   red giant
    b.   black dwarf
x   c.   black hole
    d.   white dwarf
    e.   main sequence

17. The Sun's corona is

    a.   made of a very dense gas.
x   b.   only observable during a solar eclipse.
    c.   the part of the Sun from which is emitted the light that reaches the Earth.
    d.   All of the above are true.

18.   Active regions in the Sun are probably caused by

      a.   auroras and sunspots.
      b.   turbulence due to sunspots and differential rotation.
x   c.   turbulence due to differential rotation and magnetism.
      d.   short-term changes in the Sun's luminosity.

19.   Star luminosity is

x   a.   a function of both star temperature and star size.
      b.   greater for stars of greater mass.
      c.   the same as the observed or measured brightness of the star.
      d.   a function of the colour of the material of which the star is composed.

20.   Maria Mitchell was

x   a.   the first American to discover a new comet.
      b.   married to the famous astronomer George Bond.
      c.   the first astronomer to describe an annular eclipse of the Sun.
      d.   All of the above are true.

II.   Fill-Ins

1.   A cluster of a billion or more stars, together with gas and dust, held together by gravity is called a(n) _____ .

(galaxy)

2.   When the Sun burns out its nuclear fuel it will move off the main sequence, first becoming a(n) _____ and then ending up as a(n) _____ .

(red giant...white dwarf)

3.   The total amount of energy radiated outward each second by the Sun or any other star is called the _____ .

(luminosity)

4.   The source of the Sun's energy is _____ .

(nuclear fusion) or (nuclear fusion in its core)

5.   A plot of star luminosity versus temperature is called a(n) _____ .

(Hertzsprung-Russell diagram) or (H-R diagram)

6.   When energy continuously passes through or continuously falls on a unit area, we say there is an energy _____ through or on that area.

(flux)

7.   The Sun and most other stars produce their energy by two fusion reactions: the _____ chain and the _____ chain.

(proton-proton...carbon-nitrogen-oxygen) or (PP...CNO)

8.   Venus and Mercury are too _____ for life to exist, and Mars is too _____ .

(hot...cold) or (hot & dry...cold & dry)

9.   When the path of a beam of light is bent in passing from one transparent medium into another, it is referred to as _____ .

(refraction)

10.   Visible light is just one small part of the _____ , an arrangement of electromagnetic rays in order of decreasing or increasing wavelength.

(electromagnetic spectrum)

11.   The energy created by fusion reactions in the Sun is produced in the form of _____ and _____ .

(gamma rays...neutrinos)

III. Definitions

1. blackbody radiator: a (hypothetical) perfect radiator of light that absorbs all light that strikes it and reflects none; its light output depends only on its temperature.

2. constellation: a distinctive star pattern in the sky, named mostly for animals and mythical characters.

3. electromagnetic radiation: a self-propagating electric and magnetic wave, such as light, radio, ultraviolet, or infrared radiation; all types travel at the same speed and differ in wavelength or frequency, which relates to the energy.

4. flux: the amount of energy flowing through a given area in a given time.

5. galaxy: a cluster of a billion or more stars, plus gas and dust, that is held together by gravity.

6. Hertzsprung-Russell diagram (H-R diagram): a plot of a star's luminosity versus its temperature.

7. luminosity: the total amount of energy radiated outward each second by the Sun or any other star.

8. main sequence: the principal series of stars in the Hertzsprung-Russell diagram, which includes stars that are converting hydrogen to helium.

9. red giant: a large, cool star with a high luminosity and a low surface temperature (about 2500 K), which is largely convective and has fusion reactions going on in shells.

10. reflection: the bouncing of a wave off the surface between two media.

11. refraction: the change in velocity when a wave passes from one medium to another; the process by which the path of a beam of light is bent when the beam crosses from one transparent material to another.

12. shell fusion: the process of nuclear fusion in a star, in which the hydrogen in the shell around its core is converted into helium after the hydrogen in the core itself has already been depleted; such a star becomes a red giant.

13. spectrum: a group of electromagnetic rays arranged in order of increasing or decreasing wavelength.

14. supernova: a stupendous explosion of a star, which increases its brightness hundreds of millions of times in a few days; a supernova releases heavy elements into space, and what remains of its core becomes a black hole.

15. white dwarf: a small, dense star that has exhausted its nuclear fuel and shines from residual heat; it has a high surface temperature but low luminosity.

16. zodiac: the 12 constellations through which the Sun passes.

IV. True-False Questions

1. The Sun is thought to be a fairly homogeneous body, with no internal structure or layering. (F)

2. Venus and Mars are too cold for life to exist. (F)

3. The Sun is compositionally layered, with a small rocky core inside the gigantic outer shell of gas. (F)

4. Unlike the Earth and some of the other planets, the Sun has no magnetic field. (F)

5. All telescopes work by gathering and concentrating electromagnetic radiation in the form of visible light. (F)

6. Visible light is a form of electromagnetic radiation. (T)

7. The radiative and convective layers of the Sun have approximately the same composition as that of the planet Jupiter. (T)

8. The Sun is a nearly perfect blackbody radiator. (T)

9. The photosphere is the outermost layer of the Sun, from which is emitted the light that reaches the Earth. (F)

10. Our Sun will finish its evolutionary sequence as a black dwarf in about 4 to 5 billion years. (T)

V.   Short-Answer Questions

1.   Why does the Sun appear to revolve around the Earth, when we know that the opposite is true?

Answer: The Sun appears to revolve around the Earth because of the Earth's daily rotation about its axis, which makes the Sun seem to arc across the sky from east to west every day. (This is called apparent motion.)

2.   Briefly describe the characteristics of the Sun's two outermost layers.

Answer: The Sun's two outermost layers are called the chromosphere and the corona. They are both low-density, transparent layers of very hot gas.

3.   Make a neat, well-labelled diagram showing the internal structure of the Sun.

Answer: (See Figure 2.6 in the text.)

4.   In what way might the Sun's active periods directly influence humans?

Answer: The Sun's active periods, manifested in the form of sunspots, are thought to be related to cyclical changes caused by interactions between the solar magnetic field and differential rotation. Because the Sun's magnetic field influences the Earth's outer atmosphere, many experts believe that sunspots influence the climate on the Earth.

5.   What are sunspots?

Answer: Sunspots are huge dark blotches on the surface of the Sun (actually, on the surface of the photosphere). They appear dark because they are relatively cool regions. The exact cause and mechanism of their formation is not clearly understood, but they seem to occur in cycles of about 11 years.

6.   Both the planet Jupiter and the Sun consist primarily of hydrogen and helium gas. What is the main difference between these two bodies?

Answer: The Sun is considerably more massive than Jupiter, so temperatures and pressures in the core of the Sun are high enough for nuclear fusion to occur. Nuclear fusion does not occur in the core of Jupiter.

7.   Briefly describe the characteristics of the Sun's radiative layer.

Answer: Surrounding the Sun's core is a region that is very hot but not hot enough for fusion to occur. This layer, called the radiative layer, stretches from 170,000 to 590,000 km, measuring out from the center. The energy released in the core moves across the radiative layer by radiation, and it is this layer that makes the escape of energy from the Sun a slow process. Electrons in the radiative layer absorb the γ radiation and make the layer opaque.

8.   Why is Jupiter sometimes referred to as an "almost star"?

Answer: Masses smaller than about 0.1 S are too small for the temperature in the core to get hot enough for nuclear fusion to start. Jupiter is almost (but not quite) massive enough to have nuclear fusion occurring in its core. (If Jupiter had been massive enough to become a star, our solar system would have been a binary system, with two Suns.)

VI.   Longer-Answer Questions, Essays & Critical Thinking Questions: Answers are not provided for these questions (because each student will formulate his or her answer differently), but page numbers for text references are given at the end of each question.

1.   Most of the time the Sun is relatively quiet, but sometimes it develops active regions. What are the main causes of this? (p. 55-56)

2.   What is a Hertzsprung-Russell diagram? Why are H-R diagrams important tools in the study of stellar evolution? Where does the Sun plot on a H-R diagram? (p. 59 & 62)

3.   Describe the life cycle of a 1-S star. (p. 63)

4.   How is the Principle of Uniformitarianism applied to the study of star histories? (p. 63)

5.   Describe how scientists measure changes in the Sun's luminosity. How might changes in the Sun's luminosity have affected the climate on Earth throughout its history, and how might the Earth have adjusted to these changes? (p. 57)

6.   What is the electromagnetic spectrum, and what forms of light does it contain? (p. 50-51)

7.   Describe the process of shell fusion in a 1-S star. (p. 63)

CHAPTER 3: Earthquakes and the Earth's Interior

I.   Multiple Choice Questions

1.   The amount of energy released by a Richter magnitude 7.5 earthquake is how many times greater than a magnitude 5.5 earthquake?

    a.   30
    b.   60
    c.   100
x d.   900

2.   The term epicenter refers to

    a.   the focus of an earthquake.
    b.   the point from which an earthquake's energy originates.
x c.   the point on the Earth's surface directly above the focus of an earthquake.
    d.   the point of failure of rocks in the elastic rebound theory.

3.   The term seismic gap refers to

    a.   a region where no seismic activity occurs.
    b.   the point of rupture of stressed rocks deep in the Earth (in the elastic rebound theory).
    c.   a method for predicting seismic sea waves (tsunami).
x d.   a segment of a seismically active fault along which no large earthquakes have occurred recently.

4.   An instrument which measures ground vibrations is a

    a.   gravimeter.
    b.   seismogram.
    c.   geodolite.
x d.   seismograph.

5.　　The Richter magnitude of an earthquake

　　　a.　　is measured on an instrument called a Richter scale.
x　　b.　　is measured by the amplitude of seismic waves recorded by seismographs.
　　　c.　　is determined by the area over which it is felt.
　　　d.　　depends on how near the recording instrument is to the epicenter.

6.　　Which of the following is not a danger closely associated with earthquakes?

　　　a.　　fires.
　　　b.　　seismic sea waves.
　　　c.　　quicksand.
　　　d.　　surface rupturing.
x　　e.　　heating of the ground surface.

7.　　The most intense earthquakes to jolt North America in the past 200 years were centered in

　　　a.　　California.
　　　b.　　New York.
　　　c.　　South Carolina.
x　　d.　　Missouri.

8.　　Observations which may signal an impending earthquake include

　　　a.　　swarms of tiny earthquakes.
　　　b.　　odd animal behavior.
　　　c.　　fluctuations in magnetism.
　　　d.　　tilting of the land surface.
x　　e.　　All of the above are true.

9.　　The epicenter of an earthquake is

　　　a.　　the point on a fault surface where seismic energy is first released
　　　b.　　the point from which P and S waves originate during an earthquake.
　　　c.　　the region of greatest damage during an earthquake.
x　　d.　　the point on the Earth's surface above the focus.

10.   The focus of an earthquake is

x   a.   the point on a fault surface where seismic energy is first released.
      b.   the point on the Earth's surface where seismic energy is first released.
      c.   the region of greatest damage during an earthquake.
      d.   the point on the Earth's surface above the epicenter.

11.   Which one of the following does not belong with the others?

      a.   gravimeter
x   b.   seismogram
      c.   seismograph
      d.   magnetometer

12.   The S-wave shadow zone assisted scientists in determining that

      a.   the core of the Earth is composed primarily of metallic iron and nickel.
      b.   the asthenosphere is a weak layer of anomalously low seismic velocity.
x   c.   the outer core of the Earth is molten.
      d.   All of the above are true.

13.   An increase of 1 on the Richter magnitude scale for earthquakes corresponds to an increase in released energy of approximately

      a.   10-fold.
      b.   20-fold.
x   c.   30-fold.
      d.   100-fold.

14.   An increase of 1 on the Richter magnitude scale for earthquakes corresponds to an increase in maximum seismic wave amplitude of

x   a.   10-fold.
      b.   20-fold.
      c.   30-fold.
      d.   100-fold.

15.   Tsunami

     a.   is another word for seismic wave.
x   b.   are sometimes incorrectly called tidal waves, but have nothing to do with tides.
     c.   travel very slowly across the open ocean, but hit the shore as enormous breakers.
     d.   All of the above are true.

16.   The asthenosphere

     a.   is a zone of anomalously low seismic velocity.
     b.   underlies the lithosphere.
     c.   is a zone of plastic deformation within the upper part of the mantle.
x   d.   All of the above are true.

17.   Which of the following is not a primary cause of damage by earthquakes?

     a.   liquefaction
     b.   seismic sea waves (tsunami)
     c.   collapsing regolith.
x   d.   None of these is a primary cause of damage by earthquakes.

18.   Which one of the following is not used by scientists to predict earthquakes?

     a.   foreshocks
     b.   seismic gaps
x   c.   isostasy
     d.   strange animal behavior

19.   The flotational balance among segments of the lithosphere is referred to as

     a.   gravity.
x   b.   isostasty.
     c.   density.
     d.   seismicity.

20. The asthenosphere is the zone in which

    a.   seismic wave velocities are highest.
x   b.   rocks are very ductile.
    c.   all earthquakes originate.
    d.   All of the above are true.

II.   Fill-Ins

1.   Abrupt movement of faults that releases elastically stored energy is thought to cause earthquakes: this is known as the _____ theory.

     (elastic rebound)

2.   Vibrations sent out by earthquakes are measured with an instrument called a _____ .

     (seismograph)

3.   Energy released at an earthquake's focus radiates outward as two kinds of body waves: _____ waves and _____ waves.

     (P...S) or (primary...secondary) or (compressional...shear)

4.   The pronounced seismic discontinuity which marks the mantle-crust interface is called the _____ .

     (Mohorovičić discontinuity) or (M-discontinuity) or (moho)

5.   Seismic waves that do not pass through the body of the Earth are called _____ .

     (surface waves)

6.   The _____ scale is used to calculate the amount of energy released during an earthquake.

     (Richter magnitude)

7.   The asthenosphere is a zone of anomalously _____ seismic-wave speed.

(low) or (slow)

8.   The Earth's core has a high density and is inferred to consist primarily of _____ and _____ .

(iron...nickel)

9.   The flotational balance maintained by large segments of the lithosphere which "float" on the underlying asthenosphere is referred to as _____ .

(isostasy) or (isostatic equilibrium) or (isostatic balance)

10. The scale which measures earthquake intensity on the basis of felt vibration and extent of damage to buildings is called the _____ scale.

(modified Mercalli scale) or (modified Mercalli intensity scale)

11. Rocks can be elastically deformed by seismic body waves in two ways: (1) by a change in _____ or (2) by a change in _____ .

(shape...volume)

III. Definitions

1.   body wave: seismic waves that travel outward from an earthquake focus and pass through the Earth.

2.   earthquake focus: the point of the first release of energy that causes an earthquake.

3.   elastic deformation: the reversible or nonpermanent deformation that occurs when an elastic solid is stretched and squeezed and the force is then removed.

4.   elastic rebound theory: the theory that earthquakes result from the release of stored elastic energy by slippage on faults.

5.   epicenter: that point on the Earth's surface that lies vertically above the focus of an earthquake.

6.   fault: a fracture in a rock along which movement occurs.

7.   gravity anomaly: variations in the pull of gravity after correction for latitude and altitude.

8.   isostasy: the ideal property of flotational balance among segments of the lithosphere.

9.   modified Mercalli scale: a scale used to compare earthquakes based on the intensity of damage caused by the quake.

10.   Mohorovičić discontinuity (M-discontinuity or moho): the seismic discontinuity that marks the base of the crust.

11.   P (primary) wave: seismic body waves transmitted by alternating pulses of compression and expansion; P waves pass through solids, liquids, and gases.

12.   Richter magnitude scale: a scale, based on the recorded amplitudes of seismic body waves, for comparing the amounts of energy released by earthquakes.

13.   S (secondary) wave: seismic body waves transmitted by an alternating series of sideways (shear) movements in a solid; S-waves cause a change of shape and cannot be transmitted through liquids and gases.

14.   seismic sea wave (tsunami): long wavelength ocean waves produced by sudden movement of the seafloor following an earthquake; incorrectly called tidal waves.

15.   seismic wave: elastic disturbances spreading outward from an earthquake focus.

16.   surface wave: seismic waves that are guided by the Earth's surface and to not pass through the body of the Earth.

17.   tsunami (seismic sea wave) long wavelength ocean waves produced by sudden movement of the seafloor following an earthquake; incorrectly called tidal waves.

IV.   True-False Questions

1.   The outer core is inferred to be molten because it does not transmit seismic waves. (F)

2.   When slippage of rock occurs along a fracture in a rock, the fracture is called an earthquake. (F)

3. The epicenter of an earthquake is the point where the earthquake's energy is first released. (F)

4. The point on the Earth's surface directly above the focus is called the epicenter. (T)

5. The point on the Earth's surface directly above the epicenter is called the focus. (F)

6. Seismic waves travel through the Earth at uniform velocities, spreading out in all directions. (F)

7. P waves are compressional/expansional waves that can pass through gases, liquids and solids. (T)

8. S waves travel more slowly than P waves. (T)

9. Surface waves are the first seismic waves to be recorded by the seismograph in the event of an earthquake. (F)

10. The moho is the seismic discontinuity that marks the boundary between the core and mantle of the Earth. (F)

V.   Short-Answer Questions

1.   What are six different ways earthquakes cause damage?

Answer: Earthquakes cause damage by (1) ground motion; (2) faulting and surface rupturing; (3) fires; (4) land movement and slope collapse; (5) liquefaction; and (6) tsunami.

2.   What is a seismic gap? Why are seismic gaps so important in earthquake prediction?

Answer: Seismic gaps are places along seismically active faults where, for one reason or another, earthquakes have not occurred for a long time and where elastic strain is increasing. Seismic gaps receive a lot of attention because they are considered the place most likely to experience large earthquakes.

3.   How did S-waves reveal that the Earth's outer core is liquid?

Answer: S-waves cannot be transmitted through liquids. S-waves are transmitted through the crust and mantle (solid) but not through the outer core (liquid).

4.   What does the elastic rebound theory suggest?

Answer: The elastic rebound theory suggests that, if fault surfaces lock rather than slip easily past one another, the rocks on either side of the fault will bend and in bending they will store elastic strain energy. When the fault finally does slip and the bent rocks rebound to their original shapes, an enormous amount of energy is released as an earthquake.

5.   Explain how a bent piece of wood can be an analogy for an earthquake.

Answer: When you bend a thin piece of wood, the energy from your muscles is stored in the wood in the form of elastic strain energy. If you release the wood, this stored energy will return it to its former shape. However, if you bend the wood too far it will break, and the stored elastic energy will be suddenly converted to heat energy, sound energy (the snapping of the wood), and vibrations in the wood. The same is true of rocks: when they are deformed by movement along a fault, they build up elastic strain energy. When the rock finally breaks and slippage occurs along the fault, the stored energy will be released all at once in the form of an earthquake (elastic rebound theory).

VI.   Longer-Answer Questions, Essays & Critical Thinking Questions: Answers are not provided for these questions (because each student will formulate his or her answer differently), but page numbers for text references are given at the end of each question.

1.   How are seismic waves used to learn about the internal structure of the Earth? (p. 75-77)

2.   Describe how the method of triangulation is used to locate the epicenter of an earthquake. Support you answer with a neat, well-labelled diagram. (p. 77 & 79)

3.   What does it mean when we say that the lithosphere is in isostatic balance on the asthenosphere? How does glacier ice provide a demonstration of the principle of isostasy? Support your answer with neat, well-labelled diagrams. (p. 84-86)

4.   Explain how you could use a gravimeter to demonstrate the principle of isostasy. (p. 84-85)

5.   What is an S-wave shadow zone? How have S-waves helped scientists to learn about the Earth's core? Support your answer with a neat, well-labelled diagram. (p. 75-76)

6.   Sometimes the largest earthquakes (such as the M 8.4 Good Friday earthquake in Anchorage, Alaska, 1964) cause fewer deaths than smaller earthquakes (such as the M 6.8 earthquake of December, 1988 in Armenia). Why do you think this is? (p. 79-81)

CHAPTER 4: Minerals & Rocks

I.   Multiple Choice Questions

1.   A rock is

      a.   any naturally occurring solid.
x   b.   a cohesive combination of many mineral grains.
      c.   always composed of many different minerals.
      d.   always composed of a single type of mineral.
      e.   the result of minerals crystallizing from a liquid.

2.   Scientists have identified approximately _____ minerals so far.

      a.   1500
x   b.   3500
      c.   6500
      d.   150

3.   The most common type of mineral in the crust of the Earth is

      a.   quartz.
      b.   clay.
      c.   iron.
x   d.   feldspar.

4.   The rock cycle

      a.   is more important now than ever before in Earth history.
      b.   does not involve the biosphere or the atmosphere, only the solid Earth and the hydrosphere.
x   c.   describes the processes whereby the internal activities of the solid Earth interact with external activities involving the hydrosphere, biosphere, and atmosphere.
      d.   operates independently of the process of plate tectonics.

5. The most abundant rock-forming minerals are

    a. the oxides.
x   b. the silicates.
    c. iron, nickel and sulphur.
    d. oxygen and silicon.

6. The Earth's crust is composed chiefly of

    a. nitrogen and oxygen.
    b. hydrogen and helium.
    c. nickel and iron.
x   d. oxygen and silicon.

7. Which of the following is not a mineral?

    a. diamond
x   b. oil
    c. table salt
    d. clay

8. Crystals (i.e., mineral grains with well-developed crystal faces) are uncommon in nature because

x   a. they only form when a mineral can grow freely in an open space.
    b. they are composed of rare elements.
    c. they have been mined so extensively that there are not many left.
    d. most crystals are synthesized in laboratories.

9. The texture of a rock refers to

    a. how hard or soft the rock is.
    b. how resistant the rock is to being scratched.
    c. the tendency of the rock to break in a preferred direction along planar surfaces.
x   d. the overall appearance of the rock due to the size, shape, and arrangement of its constituent mineral grains.

10. Isotopes are

    a.   atoms that have the same atomic number but different mass numbers.
    b.   atoms that have the same chemical properties but different number of protons and neutrons in their nuclei.
    c.   naturally occurring variations; most elements have several isotopes.
x   d.   All of the above are true.

11. Atoms are built up from

    a.   protons, neutrinos, and electrons.
    b.   cations and anions.
x   c.   protons, neutrons, and electrons.
    d.   elements and isotopes.
    e.   chemical compounds

12. A cation is formed when

x   a.   an atom gives up an electron and thus attains a positive electrical charge.
    b.   an atom adds an electron and thus attains a negative electrical charge.
    c.   an atom has excess electrons available for electron transfer.
    d.   None of the above is true.

13. Which one of the following does not belong with the others?

    a.   streak
    b.   color
    c.   hardness
x   d.   texture
    e.   luster

14. Which of the following is not a mineral?

    a.   gold
    b.   ice
x   c.   ivory
    d.   salt

15. Which of the following is not a required characteristic of minerals?

    a.   solid
    b.   naturally formed
x   c.   organic
    d.   characteristic crystal structure

16. The main forces that hold grains together in sedimentary rocks are

    a.   gravity and deposition.
    b.   precipitation and sedimentation.
x   c.   cementation and recrystallization.
    d.   metamorphism and recrystallization.

17. The hardest mineral is

    a.   quartz
    b.   feldspar
    c.   granite
x   d.   diamond

18. The physical properties of silicate minerals are determined, to a great extent, by

x   a.   the type and extent of polymerization of silicate tetrahedra in the crystal structure.
    b.   whether they occur in igneous, metamorphic, or sedimentary rocks.
    c.   their association with nonsilicate minerals.
    d.   None of the above is true.

19. Color is not always a reliable means of mineral identification, because

    a.   even trace amount of chemical impurities can produce distinct color differences.
    b.   in opaque minerals, color is partly a function of grain size.
    c.   two minerals with identical colors can have completely different lusters.
x   d.   All of the above are true.

20. Which one of the following does not belong with the others?

     a.   coal

x   b.   feldspar

     c.   diamond

     d.   carbon

II.   Fill-Ins

1. _____ are the most common type of minerals (95% of the crust).

   (Silicates)

2. The three families of rocks are (1) _____ ; (2) _____ ; and (3) _____ .

   (sedimentary...metamorphic...igneous)

3. The term luster refers to the _____ and _____ of light reflected from a mineral.

   (quality...intensity)

4. Scientists have identified approximately _____ minerals so far.

   (3500)

5. The silicate anion has the shape of a(n) _____ .

   (tetrahedron)

6. The _____ are the most fundamental substances into which matter can be separated by chemical means.

   (elements) or (chemical elements)

7. A(n) _____ is the smallest individual particle that retains all the properties of a given chemical element.

   (atom)

8. Solids that have a crystal structure are said to be _____ , whereas solids that lack a crystal structure are _____ .

    (crystalline...amorphous)

9. The two most common minerals in the Earth's crust are _____ and _____ .

    (feldspar...quartz)

10. When any type of rock erodes, the eroded particles form _____ .

    (sediment)

III. Definitions

1. anion: an ion with a negative electrical charge.

2. atom: the smallest individual particle that retains all the properties of a given chemical element.

3. cation: an ion with a positive electrical charge.

4. cleavage: the tendency of a mineral to break in preferred directions along bright, reflective plane surfaces.

5. crystal: a solid compound composed of ordered, three-dimensional arrays of atoms or ions chemically bonded together and displaying crystal form.

6. crystal face: the planar surfaces that bound a crystal.

7. crystal form: the geometric arrangement of crystal faces.

8. crystal structure: the geometric pattern that atoms assume in a solid; any solid that has a crystal structure is said to be crystalline.

9. density: the average mass per unit volume.

10. element (chemical): the most fundamental substance into which matter can be separated by chemical means.

11.   energy-level shell: the specific energy level of electrons as they orbit the nucleus of an atom.

12.   hardness (of a mineral): relative resistance of a mineral to scratching.

13.   igneous rock: rock formed by the cooling and consolidation of magma.

14.   ion: an atom that has excess positive or negative charges caused by electron transfer.

15.   isotope: atoms of an element having the same atomic number but differing mass numbers.

16.   luster: the quality and intensity of light reflected from a mineral.

17.   metamorphic rock: rock whose original compounds or textures, or both, have been transformed to new compounds and new textures by reactions in the solid state as a result of high temperature, high pressure, or both.

18.   midocean ridge (oceanic ridge): continuous rocky ridges on the ocean floor, hundreds of kilometers wide and a few thousand kilometers long, with a relief of more than 0.6 km.

19.   mineral: any naturally formed, crystalline solid with a definite chemical composition and a characteristic crystal structure.

20.   mineral assemblage: the variety and abundance of minerals present in a rock.

21.   sediment: regolith that has been transported by any of the external processes.

22.   sedimentary rock: any rock formed by chemical precipitation or by sedimentation and cementation of mineral grains transported to a site of deposition by water, wind, ice, or gravity.

23.   silicate: a mineral that contains the silicate anion.

24.   silicate anion (SiO_4^{-4}): a complex ion that is present in all silicate minerals.

25.   specific gravity: a number stating the ratio of the weight of a substance to the weight of an equal volume of pure water; a dimensionless number numerically equal to the density.

26.   spreading center (divergent margin): the new, growing edge of a plate; coincident with a mid-ocean ridge.

27. streak: a thin layer of powdered mineral made by rubbing a specimen on a nonglazed porcelain plate.

28. subduction zone (convergent margin): the linear zone along which a plate of lithosphere sinks down into the asthenosphere.

29: texture (of a rock): the overall appearance that a rock has because of the size, shape, and arrangement of its constituent mineral grains.

IV. True-False Questions

1. All silicate minerals contain the silicate anion as an integral part of the crystal structure. (T)

2. Scientists have found approximately 1500 minerals, and the number is rising because new ones are found each year. (F)

3. The most abundant mineral in the crust of the Earth is a silicate mineral called quartz. (F)

4. The term mineral assemblage refers to the crystal structure of a mineral and the way it is put together. (F)

5. We rely on the Principle of Uniformitarianism to tell us about changes in the magnitudes and rates of geologic processes throughout Earth history. (F)

6. Some minerals have been identified only in meteorites or in Moon rocks. (T)

7. The United States is self-sufficient in mineral resources. (F)

8. Most elements have several difference isotopes, that is, atoms with the same atomic number and chemical properties but different mass numbers. (T)

9. Nonsilicate minerals (i.e., minerals whose structures are not based on the silicate anion) are extremely rare. (F)

10. "Asbestos" is a commercial term, not a mineralogical term, used to describe a variety of minerals that occur with asbestiform habits. (T)

V. Short-Answer Questions

1. What are the four requirements that must be met in order for a substance to be called a mineral?

Answer: (1) naturally formed; (2) solid; (3) specific chemical composition; (4) characteristic crystal structure.

2. There is more igneous rock in the crust of the Earth than sedimentary rock, but we see more sedimentary rock. Explain.

Answer: (See Figure 4.8 in the text.) The crust of the Earth is composed primarily (95%) of igneous rock or metamorphic rock derived from igneous material. However, most of the rock that we actually see at the Earth's surface is sedimentary (75%), because sediments are products of weathering, and as a result they are draped as a thin veneer over the largely igneous crust below.

3. What is meant by the "texture" of a rock?

Answer: The texture of a rock is its overall appearance, resulting from the size, shape, and arrangement of its constituent mineral grains. For example, the grains may be flat and parallel to each other, giving the rock a platy texture.

4. How are rock samples prepared so they can be studied under the microscope?

Answer: Examination of rock samples under the microscope requires the preparation of a thin section of the rock. The first step is to grind and polish a smooth, flat surface on a small fragment of rock. The polished surface is glued to a glass slide, and then the rock is ground away until the glued fragment is so thin that light passes through it easily.

5. What are the eight principal properties used to characterize and identify minerals?

Answer: The principal properties used to characterize and identify minerals are: (1) crystal form; (2) growth habit; (3) cleavage; (4) luster; (5) color; (6) streak; (7) hardness; and (8) specific gravity.

VI. Longer-Answer Questions, Essays & Critical Thinking Questions: Answers are not provided for these questions (because each student will formulate his or her answer differently), but page numbers for text references are given at the end of each question.

1. Why is it important to study minerals? Try to give at least three reasons. (p. 91ff.)

2. Make a neat, well-labelled diagram illustrating the rock cycle. Briefly explain each of the major processes illustrated in your diagram. (p. 105-106)

3. List the three main families of rocks and briefly describe the processes whereby they are formed. (p. 103)

4. Rocks are coherent aggregates of many individual mineral grains. What holds them together? (p. 104-105)

CHAPTER 5: The Heat Within: Magma and Volcanoes

I. Multiple Choice Questions

1. Some magmas are more viscous than others because of their

     a. compositions.
     b. temperatures.
     c. silica contents.
x   d. All of the above are true.
     e. None of the above is true.

2. Crater Lake, Oregon, occupies the _____ left by the prehistoric eruption of Mount Mazama.

     a. volcanic neck.
     b. volcanic vent.
x   c. caldera.
     d. tephra cone.

3. By far the most important tectonic environment for the formation of explosive volcanoes is

x   a.   subduction zones.
    b.   divergent (spreading) plate boundaries.
    c.   transform plate boundaries.
    d.   intraplate "hot spots".

4. Which is the most abundant gas usually given off by volcanoes?

    a. CO_2
    b. N_2
    c. SO_2
x   d. H_2O
    e. H_2S

5. Which is the most abundant gas given off by volcanoes?

    a.   carbon dioxide
    b.   sulphur dioxide
    c.   nitrogen
x   d.   water vapour

6. Stratovolcanoes are composed of

    a.   breccia and debris.
    b.   silica-rich lavas.
    c.   runny basaltic lavas (low viscosity).
x   d.   interlayered pyroclastic material and lava flows.

7. Mount St. Helens is a typical

    a.   tephra cone volcano.
x   b.   stratovolcano.
    c.   shield volcano.
    d.   eroded volcanic neck.
    e.   fissure flow.

8. Which one of the following statements is false?

x   a. Pyroclastic activity includes ash falls, ash flows, and lava flows.
    b. Most lava flows are slow enough that people can easily move out of the way as they approach.
    c. Volcanoes in the Pacific "ring-of-fire" are generally characterized by explosive eruptions.
    d. Fires and mudflows are two serious secondary effects of volcanic activity.

9. The spectacular eruptive style of some volcanoes is due to

x   a. rapid release of magmatic gases.
    b. melting of snow at high elevations to make steam.
    c. lack of abundant silica in the magma.
    d. their elevation above sea level.
    e. the number of active volcanoes in a given region.

10. Calderas form by

    a. accumulation of thick piles of lava.
    b. accumulation of thick piles of tephra.
x   c. explosion and/or collapse within a volcanic structure.
    d. the development of lava domes.
    e. extensive fissure flows.

11. Shield volcanoes are composed primarily of low viscosity

x   a. basalt.
    b. rhyolite.
    c. andesite.
    d. granite.

12. Tephra deposits may contain

    a. volcanic glass.
    b. crystals.
    c. fragments of igneous rock.
x   d. All of the above are true.

13. Magma that reaches the surface of the Earths is called

   a. a volcanic neck.
x b. lava.
   c. basalt.
   d. tephra.

14. By definition, magma consists of

   a. molten rock.
x b. molten rock, with or without dissolved gases and suspended crystals.
   c. molten rock, with or without fragments of pyroclastic material.
   d. lava.

15. The two common igneous rocks derived from basaltic magma are

   a. basalt and granite.
   b. basalt and andesite.
x c. basalt and gabbro.
   d. granite and rhyolite.

16. Which type of magma contains the most silica (SiO_2)?

x a. rhyolite
   b. andesite
   c. basalt

17. By definition, lava is

   a. magma.
   b. molten rock with or without dissolved gases and suspended crystals.
   c. a type of pyroclastic material.
x d. magma that oozes out of a volcano.

18. Tephra is

   a. a type of pyroclastic rock.
x b. an unconsolidated deposit of pyroclastic material.
   c. a type of pyroclastic flow.
   d. a type of volcanic rock.

19. The shape of a volcanic structure is due to

    a.   gravity.
    b.   the proportions of lava and pyroclastics erupted.
    c.   the viscosities of the erupted materials.
x   d.   All of the above are true.

20. Pyroclastic flows

x   a.   can move very rapidly and may overwhelm people before they can run away.
    b.   are associated with eruptions of hot poisonous gases.
    c.   are very hot but generally move slowly enough that people can move out of the way.
    d.   occur underwater and cause tsunami.

II.   Fill-Ins

1. The three main kinds of magma are _____ , _____ , and _____ .

    (basaltic...andesitic...rhyolitic) or (basalt...andesite...rhyolite)

2. The two variables that influence the physical properties of magma the most are _____ and _____ .

    (temperature...SiO_2 content)

3. Igneous rock may be _____ , meaning it formed within the crust, or _____ , meaning it formed on the surface.

    (intrusive...extrusive) or (plutonic...volcanic)

4. In general, the higher the temperature, the _____ the viscosity of a magma.

    (lower)

5. Basalt and gabbro contain the same minerals but differ in _____ .

    (grain size)

6. The 1980 eruption of Mount St. Helens was a good example of a(n) _____ type of eruption.

   (lateral blast) or (explosive)

7. A volcano made up of lava flows, with a broad, roughly dome-shaped formation and an average surface slope of only about 5-10° is called a(n) _____ volcano.

   (shield)

8. Magma temperatures measured during eruptions range from _____ to _____ .

   (1000° C...1200° C) or (1832°F to 2192° F)

9. Smooth, ropy-looking lava is called _____ . Rubbly, rough-looking lava that forms from cooler, higher-viscosity magma is called _____ .

   (pahoehoe...aa)

10. Bubble holes trapped in lava when it solidifies are called _____ .

    (vesicles)

11. Magma is characterized by a range of compositions in which _____ is always predominant.

    (silica) or (SiO_2)

12. Magma consists of molten rock, often containing _____ and _____ .

    (gases...crystals) or (dissolved gases...suspended crystals)

III. Definitions

1. agglomerate: a pyroclastic rock consisting of bomb-sized tephra, i.e., tephra in which the average particle diameter is greater than 64 mm.

2. andesite: a fine-grained igneous rock with the composition of a diorite.

3.   basalt: a fine-grained igneous rock with the composition of a gabbro.

4.   batholith: the largest kind of pluton; a very large, igneous body of irregular shape that cuts across the layering of the rock it intrudes.

5.   Bowen's reaction series: a schematic description of the order in which different minerals crystallize during the cooling and progressive crystallization of a magma.

6.   caldera: a roughly circular, steep-walled volcanic basin several kilometers or more in diameter.

7.   dike: tabular, parallel-sided sheet of intrusive igneous rock that cuts across the layering of the intruded rock.

8.   diorite: a coarse-grained igneous rock consisting mainly of plagioclase and ferromagnesian minerals; quartz is sparse or absent.

9.   extrusive igneous rock: rock formed by the solidification of magma poured out onto the Earth's surface.

10.   gabbro: a coarse-grained igneous rock in which olivine and pyroxene are the predominant minerals and plagioclase is the feldspar present; quartz is absent.

11.   granite: a coarse-grained igneous rock containing quartz and feldspar, with potassium feldspar being more abundant than plagioclase.

12.   intrusive igneous rock: any igneous rock formed by solidification of magma below the Earth's surface.

13.   laccolith: a lenticular pluton intruded parallel to the layering of the intruded rock, above which the layers of the invaded country rock have been bent upward to form a dome.

14.   lava: magma that reaches the Earth's surface through a volcanic vent.

15.   magma: molten rock, together with any suspended mineral grains and dissolved gases, that forms when temperatures rise and melting occurs in the mantle or crust.

16.   pluton: any body of intrusive igneous rock, regardless of shape or size.

17.　porphyry: any igneous rock consisting of coarse mineral grains scattered through a mixture of fine mineral grains.

18.　pyroclast: a fragment of rock ejected during a volcanic eruption.

19.　pyroclastic rock: rocks formed from pyroclasts.

20.　rhyolite: a fine-grained igneous rock with the composition of a granite.

21.　shield volcano: a volcano that emits fluid lava and builds up a broad dome-shaped edifice with a surface slope of only a few degrees.

22.　sill: tabular, parallel-sided sheet of intrusive igneous rock that is parallel to the layering of the intruded rock.

23.　stock: a small, irregular body of intrusive igneous rock, smaller than a batholith, that cuts across the layering of the intruded rock.

24.　stratovolcano: a volcano that emits both tephra and viscous lava, and that builds up steep, conical mounds.

25.　tephra: a loose assemblage of pyroclasts.

26.　tephra cone: a cone-shaped pile of tephra deposited around a volcanic vent.

27.　tuff: a pyroclastic rock consisting of ash- or lapilli-sized tephra.

28.　viscosity: the internal property of a substance that offers resistance to flow.

29.　volcanic neck: the approximately cylindrical conduit of igneous rock forming the feeder pipe of a volcanic vent that has been stripped of its surrounding rock by erosion.

30.　volcanic pipe: a cylindrical conduit of igneous rock below a volcanic vent.

31.　volcanic rock: rock formed from the volcanic eruption of lava or tephra.

32.　volcano: the vent from which igneous matter, solid rock, debris, and gases are erupted.

33.　welded tuff (ignimbrite): pyroclastic rocks, the glassy fragments of which were plastic and so hot when deposited that they fused to form a glassy rock.

IV. True-False Questions

1. Volcanic eruptions are rare; normally there is an average of about one or two eruptions each year. (F)

2. Explosive eruptions happen primarily in volcanoes with basaltic magma, such as the Hawaiian and Icelandic volcanoes. (F)

3. The principal gas emitted by volcanoes is water vapor. (T)

4. Water vapor and carbon dioxide together make up about half of all gases emitted from volcanoes. (F)

5. Because of their low viscosities, basaltic lava flows tend to move more quickly than pyroclastic flows. (F)

6. Violent undersea eruptions can cause tsunami. (T)

7. A fissure eruption is a type of eruption in which ash and pyroclasts are ejected from a cone at the summit or along the flanks of a volcano. (F)

8. A pyroclastic flow is essentially the same as a lava flow. (F)

9. Most magmas are less dense than the solid matter from which they form. (T)

10. Magma temperatures measured during eruptions range from 1000° to 1200° C. (T)

V. Short-Answer Questions

1. Why does gas bubble out of magma when it moves towards the surface?

Answer: Pressure controls the amount of gas a magma can dissolve; more gas is dissolved at high pressure, less at low. Gas dissolved in a rising magma acts the same way as gas dissolved in soda water. When a bottle of soda is opened bubbles form because the pressure inside the bottle has dropped, allowing gas to come out of solution. Gas dissolved in an upward-moving magma also comes out of solution and forms bubbles as the pressure on the magma decreases.

2.   What is the difference between magma and lava?

Answer: Magma is molten rock (along with gases and suspended crystals) that forms at high temperature under ground. Lava is magma that reaches the Earth's surface through a volcanic vent.

3.   What is the difference between lava and pyroclasts?

Answer: Lava is magma that oozes out of a volcano and pours over the landscape. Pyroclasts are fragments of solid rock and shattered pieces of hot magma that are ejected during the course of an explosive volcanic eruption.

4.   What is the difference between pyroclasts and tephra?

Answer: Pyroclasts are fragments of solid rock and shattered pieces of hot magma that are ejected during the course of an explosive volcanic eruption. Tephra is a deposit of unconsolidated (loose) pyroclasts.

5.   Match each description with the name and date of the volcanic event:

a.   Explosive eruption of island volcano in Indian Ocean; tsunami killed 36,000

i.   Mount Pinatubo, 1990

b.   Lateral blast of Cascades Range volcano killed 62

ii.   Mont Peleé, 1902

c.   Hot, mobile pyroclastic flow from Caribbean volcano killed 29,000

iii.   Nevado del Ruiz, 1985

d.   Prehistoric eruption blasted out a huge caldera that now hosts Crater Lake

iv.   Mount St. Helens, 1980

e.   Tephra eruption from Philippines volcano destroyed U.S. airforce base

v.   Krakatau, 1883

f.   Mudflows on Colombian volcano formed when tephra combined with melting glaciers killed 20,000

vi.   Mount Mazama, ca. 4600 B.C.

Answer: a-v; b-iv; c-ii; d-vi; e-i; f-iii

6.   Why is tephra sometimes dangerous long after an eruption has ceased?

Answer: Rain or melt water from snow can loosen tephra piled on a steep volcanic slope and start a deadly mudflow.

7.   How are temperature, composition, and viscosity interrelated in magmas?

Answer: Magma viscosity depends on temperature and composition, especially the SiO_2 content. The higher the silica content, the more viscous the magma. The higher the temperature, the less viscous the magma.

8.   What is the "Ring of Fire"?

Answer: The Ring of Fire is a ring of explosive andesitic volcanoes surrounding the Pacific Ocean rim, parallel to plate subduction margins.

VI.   Longer-Answer Questions, Essays & Critical Thinking Questions: Answers are not provided for these questions (because each student will formulate his or her answer differently), but page numbers for text references are given at the end of each question.

1.   Why is the study of volcanoes relevant to Earth system science? (p. 114)

2.   How does Bowen's reaction series account for the different types of magmas and rocks that occur in the Earth? (p. 126-127)

3.   What is fractional melting, and how can this process account for the formation of different magma types? (p. 131-132)

4.   Describe how the process of volcanism renews the surface of the land. (p. 124)

5.   Summarize the main types of hazards associated with volcanic eruptions. (p. 123)

6.   Discuss the relationship between the tectonic cycle and the locations of different types of volcanoes. (p. 130-131)

7.   Compare and contrast the proposed modes of formation of the three main magma types: basaltic, andesitic, and volcanic. (p. 130-132)

8.   Describe how rocks are named according to textures and mineral assemblages. (p. 128-129)

CHAPTER 6: The Principles of Plate Tectonics

I.   Multiple Choice Questions

1.   The Himalayan mountains represent a modern example of a

x   a.   continent-continent collisional plate boundary.
     b.   continent-ocean collisional plate boundary.
     c.   subduction zone collisional plate boundary.
     d.   transform plate boundary.

2.   Earthquakes are

     a.   restricted to plate boundaries.
x   b.   most common along plate boundaries.
     c.   evenly distributed across plates.
     d.   most common in ocean basins.

3.   Which one of the following statements is false?

     a.   The minerals in lava crystallize at temperatures well above the Curie point of
           magnetite.
     b.   As the crystallized lava cools, the temperature drops below the Curie point.
x   c.   When the temperature of magnetite drops below its Curie point, the magnetite loses its
           permanent magnetism.
     d.   The grains of magnetite in a solidified lava will carry a record of the Earth's magnetic
           field at the moment the lava cooled below the Curie point.

4.   Which one of the following does not belong with the others?

     a.   subduction
     b.   convergent margin
     c.   island arc
x   d.   spreading center
     e.   stratovolcano

5. Transform plate boundaries are characterized by

x   a. earthquakes.
    b. volcanic activity.
    c. mountain building.
    d. All of the above are true.

6. The "plates" referred to in the theory of plate tectonics are

x   a. relatively thin slabs of rigid rock floating on the mantle.
    b. defined by their relative thickness.
    c. formed around the major continents.
    d. defined by their relative densities.

7. Midocean ridges define

    a. convergent plate boundaries.
    b. shear plate boundaries.
x   c. divergent plate boundaries.
    d. All of the above are true.

8. Which one of the following does not belong with the others?

    a. divergent margin
    b. continental rift
x   c. stratovolcano
    d. midocean ridge
    e. seafloor spreading

9. Alfred Wegener

    a. was the first to propose the hypothesis of continental drift.
x   b. amassed an impressive body of evidence in support of the hypothesis of continental drift.
    c. used paleomagnetism to prove the hypothesis of seafloor spreading and continental drift.
    d. All of the above are true.

10. The Earth's magnetic field is caused by

    a.   the rotation of the planet.
    b.   flow of molten iron in the outer core.
    c.   electrical currents in the outer core.
x   d.   All of the above are true.

11. Reversals of the Earth's magnetic poles

    a.   are not very well understood.
    b.   provided evidence, through paleomagnetism, for seafloor spreading.
    c.   are recorded in the permanent magnetism of lavas millions of years old.
x   d.   All of the above are true.

12. The number of large lithospheric plates is

    a.   ten.
x   b.   six.
    c.   about twenty.
    d.   too many to count.

13. Which one of the following statements is false?

x   a.   The mid-ocean spreading ridge environment, although characterized by volcanism, is mainly aseismic (non-seismic).
    b.   Most deep-focus earthquakes are located along convergent plate margins.
    c.   The majority of circum-Pacific area earthquakes are associated with the process of subduction.
    d.   The Pacific Plate, on the west side of the San Andreas Fault, is moving roughly northwards relative to the North American Plate, on the east side of the fault.

14. We can determine absolute plate motions by reference to

    a.   other plates.
x   b.   hot spots.
    c.   the positions of volcanoes in the Earth's crust.
    d.   midocean ridges.

15. Convergent margins

   x   a.   occur where two plates are moving toward each other.
          b.   are characterized by the formation of oceanic trenches.
          c.   involve the formation of new continental crust.
          d.   All of the above are true.

16. The African Rift is a modern example of a

   x   a.   divergent plate margin within continental crust.
          b.   new ocean forming.
          c.   subduction zone.
          d.   continent-continent collision zone.

17. Which one of the following does not belong with the others?

          a.   subduction zone
          b.   island arc
          c.   deep-sea trench
   x   d.   rifting

18. A linear zone along which a plate of lithosphere sinks down into the asthenosphere is called a(n)

   x   a.   subduction zone.
          b.   magmatic arc
          c.   island arc
          d.   continental slope

19. The geological edge of an ocean basin is at the bottom of the

          a.   continental crust.
   x   b.   continental slope.
          c.   continental shelf.
          d.   abyssal plain.

20.   A collision zone marks

      a.   the disappearance of an ocean.
      b.   the convergence of two plates capped by continental crust.
      c.   the tectonic setting in which spectacular mountain ranges are uplifted.
x   d.   All of the above are true.

II.   Fill-Ins

1.   The hypothesis that new oceanic crust is created at midocean ridges by magma rising from deep inside the Earth is called _____ .

(seafloor spreading)

2.   Divergent margins are also called _____ .

(spreading centers)

3.   The two main types of convergent margins are _____ and _____ .

(subduction zones...continental collisions)

4.   The geological edge of an ocean basin is at the bottom of the _____ .

(continental slope)

5.   The deepest parts of the ocean are the _____ associated with subduction zones.

(trenches)

6.   The western margin of South America is an example of a present-day _____ .

(subduction zone) or (convergent margin)

7.   The San Andreas Fault is an example of a(n) _____ type of plate boundary.

(transform) or (transform fault)

8. The fastest-moving plates are the Pacific and Nazca plates, which move at a speed of about
    _____ .

    (9 cm/yr) or (3.5 in/yr)

III. Definitions

1. abyssal plain: a large flat area of the deep seafloor having slopes less than about 1 m/km, and ranging in depth below sea level from 3 to 6 km.

2. collision margin: convergent margin.

3. continental rise: a region of gently changing slope where the floor of the ocean basin meets the margin of a continent.

4. continental shelf: a submerged platform of variable width that forms a fringe around a continent.

5. continental slope: a pronounced slope beyond the seaward margin of the continental shelf.

6. convergent margin: the zone where plates meet as they move toward each other; subduction zone.

7. Curie point: a temperature above which permanent magnetism is not possible.

8. divergent margin (spreading center): a fracture in the lithosphere where two plates move apart.

9. paleomagnetism: remanent magnetism in ancient rock recording the direction of the magnetic poles at some time in the past.

10. seafloor spreading: a theory proposed during the early 1960s in which lateral movements of the oceanic crust away from midocean ridges was postulated.

11. spreading center (divergent margin): the new, growing edge of a plate; coincident with a midocean ridge.

12. subduction zone (convergent margin): the linear zone along which a plate of lithosphere sinks down into the asthenosphere.

13. transform fault margin: a fracture in the lithosphere along which two plates slide past each other.

IV. True-False Questions

1. Iron-bearing minerals lose their magnetism above the Curie point. (T)

2. The solid Earth, unlike the other reservoirs of the Earth system, is constant and unchanging. (F)

3. Paleomagnetism is a property of rocks which records the directions of ancient magnetic fields at the time of rock formation. (T)

4. Sedimentary rocks cannot acquire permanent magnetism, only rocks crystallized from a magma can become permanently magnetized. (F)

5. The San Andreas Fault in California is an example of a subduction zone type of plate margin. (F)

6. The Alps, the Urals, the Himalaya, and the Appalachians are all examples of ancient divergent plate margins. (F)

7. The Sierra Nevada of California is an example of an ancient magmatic arc, evidence that the western margin of North America was once a subduction zone. (T)

8. The African Rift Valley is an example of a present-day continental divergent margin. (T)

9. The topographic expression of a spreading center is a midocean ridge formed as a result of volcanism. (T)

10. Continental crust is thicker than oceanic crust. (T)

V. Short-Answer Questions

1. What is the source of the Earth's magnetism?

Answer: The source of the Earth's magnetism is the outer core, which is molten.

2.   What is a hot spot?

Answer: A hot spot is a long-lived magma source deep within the mantle. Sometimes they cause intraplate volcanism, as in the Hawaiian chain of volcanic islands. The lithosphere appears to move over hot spots, because they are so deep-seated, so they can be used as reference points in studying the absolute motion of plates.

3.   Why was Wegener's hypothesis of continental drift not widely accepted when it was first proposed?

Answer: In spite of the impressive evidence presented by Wegener in favor of continental drift, the hypothesis was not widely accepted because no one could explain how a solid, rocky continent could possibly overcome friction and slide across the oceanic crust.

4.   What is a Benioff Zone?

Answer: A Benioff Zone is a region inside the Earth where very deep focus earthquakes occur. These slanting zones are the places where old lithosphere is sinking into the asthenosphere. (See Fig. 6.8 in the text)

5.   Draw neat, well-labelled diagrams to illustrate the difference between a convergent margin where subduction is occurring and a convergent margin where continental collision is occurring.

Answer: (See Fig. 6.11B & C in the text.)

6.   What is the source of the energy that drives plate motion?

Answer: The Earth's internal energy drives plate motion. (or) Convection in the mantle drives plate motion.

VI.   Longer-Answer Questions, Essays & Critical Thinking Questions: Answers are not provided for these questions (because each student will formulate his or her answer differently), but page numbers for text references are given at the end of each question.

1.   How did paleomagnetic evidence lead to the acceptance of the hypothesis of seafloor spreading? (p. 140-141)

2.   Describe how satellite data can help scientists study plate motion. (p. 142-143)

3. Describe the three main types of plate margins. (p. 147)

4. Describe the process whereby a continental rift can evolve into a new ocean. (p. 148)

5. Discuss the mechanisms proposed to explain lithospheric motion in plate tectonics. (p. 154)

6. What is the difference between absolute motion and relative motion, and why is this difference relevant to the study of lithospheric plates? (p. 144-146)

7. Describe the major topographic features of the ocean floor, and place them in the context of plate tectonic theory. (p. 148-150)

8. The identification of the asthenosphere as a zone of weak, fluidlike material with low seismic velocities was critical in formulating the theory of plate tectonics. Why? (p. 142)

9. How did the discovery of apparent polar wandering lend support to the hypothesis of continental drift? (p. 140)

CHAPTER 7: The Earth's Evolving Crust

I.   Multiple Choice Questions

1. Which one of the following is not a type of metamorphic rock?

     a.   marble
     b.   slate
x   c.   shale
     d.   gneiss

2. Which one of the following is not a type of chemical sedimentary rock?

x   a.   peat
     b.   coal
     c.   limestone
     d.   salt

3.   Which one of the following does not belong with the others?

      a.   unconformity
      b.   nonconformity
x   c.   subconformity
      d.   disconformity

4.   Which one of the following is not a term that is used to describe clastic sedimentary rocks?

      a.   varved
      b.   cross-bedded
      c.   well sorted
x   d.   foliated

5.   The principle of stratigraphic superposition states that

x   a.   in any sequence of sedimentary strata, the order in which the strata were deposited is from the bottom to the top.
      b.   older strata are deformed and truncated by erosion before younger strata are deposited across them.
      c.   tectonics, erosion, and sedimentation are all closely related.
      d.   sediments are deposited in strata that are horizontal, or nearly so, and parallel to the Earth's surface.

6.   English land surveyor William Smith is remembered for having been the first to recognize that

      a.   radioactive isotopes can be used to determine the absolute ages of rock formations.
      b.   biogenic sediments form as a result of biochemical reactions in water.
x   c.   rock strata can be correlated from one locality to another over distances of many kilometers.
      d.   an unconformity is a break or gap in the sedimentary record, representing a period of nondeposition and erosion.

7.   Sediment derived from the breakdown of previous rocks is called _____ sediment.

      a.   biogenic
      b.   chemical
      c.   low-grade
x   d.   clastic

8. Varves are

      a.   ancient cross-bedded sand dunes.
      b.   a type of biogenic sediment.
x   c.   pairs of sedimentary layers formed over the cycle of a single year.
      d.   chemical sediments formed as the result of evaporation.

9. The intergranular fluid present in the pore space of rocks

      a.   generally consists of pure water.
x   b.   may contain small amounts of dissolved salts.
      c.   is usually not involved in the process of metamorphism.
      d.   slows down the process of metamorphism by cooling the rocks.

10. Cross bedding

      a.   can reveal the direction in which the related current of water or air was flowing at the time of deposition.
      b.   consist of clasts coarser than silt and are the work of turbulent flow in streams, wind, or ocean waves.
      c.   refers to sedimentary beds that are inclined with respect to a thicker stratum within which they occur.
x   d.   All of the above are true.

11. Which one of the following does not belong with the others?

      a.   coquina
      b.   chalk
      c.   limestone
x   d.   tillite

12. Three large and three small cratons became welded together to form the Canadian Shield, about _____ years ago.

      a.   2.5 billion
      b.   4.6 billion
x   c.   1.6 billion
      d.   2.5 million

13. Foliation is

  x   a.   a planar texture found in some metamorphic rocks.
           b.   formed in metamorphic rocks as a result of uniform stress.
           c.   a rock texture that is typical of burial metamorphism.
           d.   essentially the same as bedding.

14. Where would you go to find burial metamorphism occurring today?

  x   a.   Gulf of Mexico
           b.   Himalaya
           c.   San Andreas Fault
           d.   Appalachians

15. Where would you go to find regional metamorphism occurring today?

           a.   Appalachians
           b.   California
           c.   Gulf of Mexico
  x   d.   Himalaya

16. Where would you go to find blueschist facies (high pressure, low temperature) metamorphism occurring today?

  x   a.   Aleutian Islands
           b.   California
           c.   Gulf of Mexico
           d.   Appalachians

17. A craton is

           a.   a stable platform.
  x   b.   a core of very ancient rock.
           c.   a continental shield.
           d.   All of the above are true.

18. A modern example of a plate triple junction is found in the area of

x a.   the Red Sea and the Gulf of Aden.
     b.   the Aleutian Islands.
     c.   the Canadian Shield.
     d.   the Andean coast of South America.

19. Which one of the following mountain chains is <u>not</u> still being actively uplifted?

     a.   Alps
     b.   Himalaya
x c.   Appalachians
     d.   Carpathians

20. Finnish geologist Pennti Eskola is remembered for having proposed

     a.   the principle of stratigraphic superposition.
     b.   the law of original horizontality.
     c.   the principle of uniformitarianism.
x d.   the concept of metamorphic facies.

II.   Fill-Ins

1. The two basic laws underlying stratigraphy are: (1) _____ and (2) _____ .

   (the law of original horizontality...the principle of stratigraphic superposition)

2. Sediment is lithified to sedimentary rock by _____ or _____ of the sediment particles.

   (cementation...recrystallization)

3. Substantial breaks or gaps in the sedimentary record are called _____ .

   (unconformities)

4. The absolute ages of strata in the geologic column have been determined by _____ .

   (radiometric age dating)

5. There are two families of sediment: (1) _____ and (2) _____ .

    (clastic...chemical)

6. Metamorphism occurs in the solid state as a result of changes in _____ and _____ .

    (temperature...pressure)

7. The type of metamorphism that occurs along subduction zones and collision edges of plates is _____ .

    (regional metamorphism)

8. The type of metamorphism that occurs within the thick piles of sediment at the foot of continental slopes and in submarine fans off the mouths of the world's great river systems is _____ .

    (burial metamorphism)

9. Chemical sediment formed as the result of evaporation is called a(n) _____ .

    (evaporite)

10. The ancient, tectonically and isostatically stable portions of the continental crust are called _____ .

    (cratons)

11. A sediment having a wide range of clast size is said to be _____ .

    (poorly sorted)

12. A pair of sedimentary layers deposited over the cycle of a single year is called a _____ .

    (varve)

13. There are five kinds of continental margins: (1) _____ , (2) _____ ,
    (3) _____ , (4) _____ , (5) _____ .

    (passive...convergent...collision...transform fault...accreted terrane)

14. When chemical sediment forms as a result of biochemical reactions in water, the resulting sediment is said to be _____ .

(biogenic)

15. _____ is the initial stage in the development of the biogenic sedimentary rock we call coal.

(Peat)

16. The three important types of unconformities are (1) _____ , (2) _____ , and (3) _____ .

(nonconformity...angular unconformity...disconformity)

17. The transformation of sediment to sedimentary rock is called _____ , which comes from the Greek word meaning "stone."

(lithification)

18. In metamorphic rocks containing sheet-structure minerals, differential stress often leads to the formation of a planar texture called _____ .

(foliation)

III. Definitions

1. accreted terrane: block of crust moved laterally by strike-slip faulting or by a combination of strike-slip faulting and subduction, then accreted to a larger mass of continental crust; also called a suspect terrane.

2. amphibolite: a metamorphic rock of intermediate grade, generally coarse-grained, containing abundant amphibole.

3. bed: the smallest formal unit of a body of sediment or sedimentary rock.

4. bedding: the layered arrangement of strata in a body of sediment or sedimentary rock.

5. burial metamorphism: metamorphism caused solely by the burial of sedimentary or pyroclastic rocks.

6. chemical sediment: sediment formed by precipitation of minerals from solutions in water.

7. clastic sediment: the loose fragmented debris produced by the mechanical breakdown of older rocks.

8. coal: a black, combustible, sedimentary or metamorphic rock consisting chiefly of decomposed plant matter and containing more than 50 percent organic matter.

9. conglomerate: a sedimentary rock composed of clasts of rounded gravel set in a finer grained matrix.

10. continental shield: an assemblage of cratons and orogens that has reached isostatic equilibrium.

11. craton: a core of ancient rock in the continental crust that has attained tectonic and isostatic stability.

12. cross bedding: beds that are inclined with respect to a thicker stratum within which they occur.

13. differential stress: stress in a solid that is not equal in all directions.

14. dolostone: a sedimentary rock composed chiefly of the mineral dolomite.

15. foliation: the planar texture of mineral grains, principally micas, produced by metamorphism.

16. fossil: the naturally preserved remains or traces of an animal or a plant.

17. geologic column: a composite diagram combining in chronological order the succession of known strata, fitted together on the basis of their fossils or other evidence of relative or actual age.

18. gneiss: a high-grade metamorphic rock, always coarse-grained and foliated, with marked compositional layering but with imperfect cleavage.

19. greenschist: a low-grade metamorphic rock rich in chlorite.

20. limestone: a sedimentary rock consisting chiefly of calcium carbonate, mainly in the form of the mineral calcite.

21. marble: a metamorphic rock derived from limestone and consisting largely of calcite.

22. metamorphic facies: contrasting assemblages of minerals that reach equilibrium during a metamorphism within a specific range of physical conditions belonging to the same metamorphic facies.

23. metamorphism: all changes in mineral assemblage and rock texture, or both, that take place in sedimentary and igneous rocks in the solid state within the Earth's crust as a result of changes in temperature and pressure.

24. original horizontality (law of): waterlaid sediments are deposited in strata that are horizontal, or nearly horizontal, and parallel, or nearly parallel, to the Earth's surface.

25. orogen: elongate region of the crust that has been intensively folded, faulted, and thickened as a result of continental collision.

26. peat: an unconsolidated deposit of plant remains that is the first stage in the conversion of plant matter to coal.

27. phyllite: a well-foliated metamorphic rock in which the component platy minerals are just visible.

28. quartzite: a metamorphic rock consisting largely of quartz, and derived from a sandstone.

29. regional metamorphism: metamorphism affecting large volumes of crust and involving both mechanical and chemical changes.

30. sandstone: a medium-grained clastic sedimentary rock composed chiefly of sand-sized grains.

31. schist: a well-foliated metamorphic rock in which the component platy minerals are clearly visible.

32. shale: a fine-grained, clastic sedimentary rock.

33. siltstone: a sedimentary rock composed mainly of silt-sized mineral fragments.

34. slate: a low-grade metamorphic rock with a pronounced slaty cleavage.

35. stratification: the layered arrangement of sediments, sedimentary rocks, or extrusive igneous rocks.

36. stratigraphic superposition (principle of): in a sequence of strata, not later overturned, the order in which they were deposited is from bottom to top.

37. stratigraphy: the study of strata.

38. stratum (plural = strata): a distinct layer of sediment that accumulated at the Earth's surface.

39. unconformity: a substantial break or gap in a stratigraphic sequence that marks the absence of part of the rock record.

40. uniform stress: stress that is equal in all directions; also called confining stress or homogeneous stress.

41. varve: a pair of sedimentary layers deposited during the seasonal cycle of a single year.

IV. True-False Questions

1. The two main families of sediments are clastic and burial sediments. (F)

2. An unconformity is a place in the rock record where one type of rock stratum ends and another begins. (F)

3. Sedimentary stratification results from the arrangement of sedimentary particles in layers. (T)

4. Varves are sedimentary layers that are inclined with respect to a thicker stratum within which they occur. (F)

5. Biogenic sediments can form both in the sea and on land. (T)

6. An angular unconformity implies that the older strata were deformed and then truncated by erosion before younger strata were deposited across them. (T)

7. The geologic column places known strata in chronological order on the basis of their fossils or other evidence of relative age. (T)

8. Shale is a type of sedimentary rock made of fine sand and silt particles cemented together. (F)

9. A passive continental margin is one that occurs in the stable interior of a plate. (T)

10. Correlation means the determination of equivalence in age of strata found in more than one locality. (T)

V.   Short-Answer Questions

1. Describe the two main families of sediment.

Answer: (1) Clastic sediment consists of bits of broken rock and minerals that are moved as solid particles. (2) Chemical sediment is transported in solution and deposited when the dissolved minerals are precipitated.

2. What is the difference between a craton and a continental shield?

Answer: A craton is a core of very ancient rock. A continental shield is a composite assemblage of cratons interspersed with ancient orogens, belts of former mountain-building activity.

3. What is regional metamorphism, and where does it occur?

Answer: Regional metamorphism involves the mechanical deformation and chemical recrystallization of tens of thousands of square kilometers of rock. It occurs during both subduction and collisions between continents, when rocks along the margin of a continent are subjected to intense differential stress and high temperatures.

4. What is burial metamorphism, and where does it occur?

Answer: Burial metamorphism occurs when sediments and/or pyroclastics are buried deep in sedimentary basins, such as in deep-sea trenches on the margins of tectonic plates and off the mouths of great rivers. In such deep basins temperatures may be in excess of 200° C (392° F), and pore water present in the buried sediments speeds up the chemical recrystallization of the rocks.

5. What are the two basic laws upon which stratigraphy is based? Briefly explain each of them.

Answer: (1) The law of original horizontality states that sediments are deposited in strata that are horizontal, or nearly so, and parallel to the Earth's surface. (2) The principle of stratigraphic superposition states that in any sequence of sedimentary strata the order in which the strata were deposited is from the bottom to the top.

6. What kind of continental margin is represented by the eastern coast of North America?

Answer: A passive continental margin.

7. What kind of continental margin is represented by the western coast of South America?

Answer: A continental convergent margin (a subduction zone).

8. What kind of continental margin is represented by the western coast of North America, from the Gulf of California to San Francisco?

Answer: A transform fault margin.

9. What kind of continental margin is represented by the Alpine-Himalaya mountain chain?

Answer: A continental collision margin.

10. What kind of continental margin is represented by the western coast of North America from central California to Alaska?

Answer: An accreted terrane margin.

VI. Longer-Answer Questions, Essays & Critical Thinking Questions: Answers are not provided for these questions (because each student will formulate his or her answer differently), but page numbers for text references are given at the end of each question.

1. What are the five types of continental margin? Describe how they form, in the context of the theory of plate tectonics. Give modern-day examples of each type of continental margin. (p. 180-184)

2. What is the difference between the relative age and the absolute age of a rock formation? Which type of age does a geologist deal with? (p. 163-165)

3. How does the theory of plate tectonics account for the different metamorphic facies that form during regional metamorphism? A well-labelled diagram would be an appropriate way to answer this question. (p. 177-179 and Figs. 7.14 & 7.15)

4. Describe how radioactive isotopes can be used to determine the absolute age of a rock formation. (p. 164-165)

5. How are clastic sedimentary rocks classified? Give examples of the principal kinds of clastic sediment and the rocks formed from them. (p. 167-168)

CHAPTER 8: The World Ocean

I. Multiple Choice Questions

1. Approximately what proportion of the Earth's surface is covered by seawater?

    a. 65%
    b. 83%
x   c. 71%
    d. 52%

2. Which one of the following does not belong with the others?

x   a. mesocline
    b. thermocline
    c. halocline
    d. pycnocline

3. Which one of the following does not refer to the vertical stratification of ocean water?

x   a. mesocline
    b. thermocline
    c. halocline
    d. pycnocline

4. The greatest ocean depth yet measured is just over _____ .

    a. 2 km
    b. 3.8 km
x   c. 11 km
    d. 23 km

5. The oceanic flow phenomenon first observed by Norwegian explorer Fridtjof Nansen during his voyage across the frozen Arctic Ocean was subsequently named

x   a. Ekman transport.
    b. El Niño/Southern Oscillation
    c. the Coriolis effect.
    d. Nansen flow.

6. El Niños can cause

    a. failure of the Indian monsoon.
    b. anomalous cyclones in Hawaii.
    c. adverse effects on fishing off the coast of Peru.
    d. drought conditions in Australia.
x   e. All of the above are true.

7. The periodic climatic variation in which tradewinds slacken and surface waters of the central and eastern Pacific become anomalously warm is called

x   a. El Niño/Southern Oscillation.
    b. thermohaline circulation.
    c. geostrophic flow.
    d. Ekman transport.

8. The ions responsible for the salinity of seawater come from

    a. dissolved minerals in stream water.
    b. gases released during volcanic eruptions.
    c. dust eroded from desert regions and blown out to sea.
    d. pollution from human activity.
x   e. All of the above are true.

9. Which one of the following does not belong with the others?

x   a. subduction
    b. downwelling
    c. upwelling
    d. Ekman transport

10. The four major basins of the world ocean are

     a. the Pacific, Atlantic, Arctic, and Southern Oceans.
     b. the Atlantic, Pacific, Mediterranean, and Indian Oceans.
x   c. the Atlantic, Pacific, Indian, and Southern Oceans.
     d. the Arctic, Atlantic, Pacific, and Indian Oceans.

11. The topography of the seafloor is

     a. known in great detail due to thousands of echo soundings made over the past 70 years.
x   b. known in considerable detail for all but the most remote parts of the ocean basins.
     c. still not very well known or understood.
     d. similar from one major basin to another.

12. The salinity of seawater is expressed in units of "per mil," which means

     a. parts per million.
     b. percent per million.
x   c. parts per thousand.
     d. parts per hundred.

13. North Atlantic Deep Water (NADW) is

     a. the central water mass of the Atlantic.
     b. the most extensive cold water body in the world ocean.
x   c. a dense, cold, saline deep-water mass in the North Atlantic that extends from the intermediate water to the ocean floor.
     d. All of the above are true.

14. Which one of the following does not belong with the others?

      a.   gypsum
      b.   carnalite
x   c.   phyllite
      d.   halite

15. The heat capacity of water is _____ that of most other substances.

      a.   about the same as
      b.   much lower than
x   c.   much higher than
      d.   not comparable to

16. Surface ocean currents are broad, slow drifts of surface water set in motion by

      a.   the Coriolis effect.
      b.   Ekman transport.
      c.   the tidal force.
x   d.   prevailing surface winds.

17. The Sargasso Sea provides a good example of

x   a.   geostrophic flow.
      b.   Ekman transport.
      c.   the Southern Oscillation.
      d.   thermohaline circulation.

18. Wave activity that occurs between the line of breakers and the shore is called

      a.   refraction.
x   b.   surf.
      c.   a longshore current.
      d.   a wave base.

19. Tsunami can be caused by

      a.   submarine landslides.
      b.   large earthquakes.
      c.   submarine volcanic eruptions.
x   d.   All of the above are true.

20. Sea levels fluctuate as a result of

      a.   changes in water volume due to the waxing and waning of continental glaciers.
      b.   changes in ocean-basin volume as lithospheric plates shift their positions.
      c.   tidal forces.
x   d.   All of the above are true.

21. A flow of surface water around the outside edges of a gyre is called a(n)

      a.   El Niño.
x   b.   geostrophic current.
      c.   thermohaline current.
      d.   Coriolis flow.

22. The world has had liquid water on its surface since at least _____ years ago.

      a.   3.95 million
x   b.   3.95 billion
      c.   4.55 billion
      d.   4.55 million

II. Fill-Ins

1. Seawater covers nearly _____ percent of the Earth's surface.

(71)

2. The world has had liquid water on its surface since at least _____ years ago.

(3.95 billion)

3. The pycnocline is a zone in which the _____ of seawater changes rapidly with increasing depth.

(density)

4. The halocline is a zone in which the _____ of seawater changes rapidly with increasing depth.

(salinity)

5. Both the _____ and the _____ of seawater are closely related to latitude.

(surface temperature...surface salinity)

6. The Coriolis effect deflects ocean currents to the _____ in the northern hemisphere and to the _____ in the southern hemisphere.

(right...left)

7. A(n) _____ is a wall of water a meter or more high, which results when an incoming tide becomes amplified as it moves rapidly up a narrow bay, strait, or estuary.

(tidal bore)

8. Near coasts, Ekman transport can lead to vertical movement of ocean water. When the net transport is away from the land, _____ occurs; when the net transport is towards the land, _____ occurs.

(upwelling...downwelling)

9. The major _____ circulation cells that make up the global ocean conveyor system involve both the temperature and salinity characteristics of the ocean waters, and are driven by the exchange of heat and moisture between the atmosphere and the ocean.

(thermohaline)

10. The thermocline is a zone in which the _____ of seawater changes rapidly with increasing depth.

(temperature)

III. Definitions

1. Coriolis effect: an effect that causes any body that moves freely with respect to the rotating solid Earth to veer toward the right in the northern hemisphere and toward the left in the southern hemisphere, regardless of the initial direction of the moving body.

2. downwelling: the process by which surface water thickens and sinks.

3. Ekman spiral: a spiraling current pattern from the water's surface to deeper layers, caused by the Coriolis effect, as each successive, slower moving layer of water is shifted to the right.

4. Ekman transport: the average flow of water in a current over the full depth of the Ekman spiral.

5. El Niño/Southern Oscillation (ENSO): a periodic climatic variation in which tradewinds slacken and surface waters of the central and eastern Pacific become anomalously warm.

6. emergence: an increase in the area of land exposed above sea level resulting from uplift of the land and/or fall of the sea level.

7. evaporite deposits: layers of salts that precipitate as a consequence of evaporation.

8. geostrophic current: a flow of surface water around a gyre that is not deflected toward the center of the gyre.

9. gyre: a large subcircular current system of which each major ocean current is a part.

10. halocline: a zone of the ocean, below the surface zone, which is marked by a substantial increase of salinity with depth.

11. heat capacity: the amount of heat required to raise or lower the temperature of a material.

12. North Atlantic Deep Water (NADW): a deep-ocean mass in the North Atlantic that extends from the intermediate water to the ocean floor; dense and cold, it originates at several sites near the surface of the North Atlantic, flows downward, and spreads southward into the South Atlantic.

13. pycnocline: an ocean zone beneath the surface zone in which water density increases rapidly, as a result of a decrease in temperature, and increase in salinity, or both.

14. salinity: the measure of the sea's saltiness; expressed in parts per thousand.

15. submergence: a rise of water level relative to the land so that areas formerly dry are inundated.

16. surf: wave activity between the line of breakers and the shore.

17. thermocline: a zone of ocean water lying beneath the surface zone, characterized by a marked decrease in temperature.

18. thermohaline circulation: global patterns of water circulation propelled by the sinking of dense cold and salty water.

19. tsunami (seismic sea waves): long wavelength ocean waves produced by sudden movement of the seafloor following an earthquake; incorrectly called tidal waves.

20. upwelling: the process by which subsurface waters flow upward and replace the water moving away.

21. wave base: the effective lower limit of wave motion, which is half of the wavelength.

22. wavelength: the distance between the crests or troughs of adjacent waves.

23. wave refraction: the process by which the direction of a series of waves, moving into shallow water at an angle to the shoreline, is changed.

24. western boundary current: a current that flows generally poleward, parallel to a continental coastline; the poleward direction is caused by the deflection of westward-flowing equatorial currents as they encounter land.

IV. True-False Questions

1. A line connecting points of equal temperature is called an isocline. (F)

2. Each major ocean current is part of a large subcircular current system called a gyro. (F)

3. Most of the water on the Earth is contained in three interconnected basins—the Pacific, Atlantic, and Indian oceans. (T)

4. The average salinity of seawater is about 35%. (F)

5. The most important ions in seawater are Na$^+$ and Cl$^-$, the constituents of common salt. (T)

6. The most important salts that precipitate from seawater, forming evaporite deposits, are gypsum, halite, and carnalite. (T)

7. The highest salinities in ocean water are found near the poles. (F)

8. The ocean differs from the land in that water has a higher heat capacity. (T)

9. Surface waves on the oceans receive their energy from winds blowing across the water surface. (T)

10. Wave forms in water are created by a looplike motion of water parcels, in which the diameter of the loops at the water surface exactly equal the wave height. (T)

11. Wave refraction occurs when currents are deflected by the Coriolis effect. (F)

12. Tides are caused by the gravitational attraction between the Moon and the Earth. (T)

V. Short-Answer Questions

1. If dissolved ions are always being added to the ocean, why is ocean water not more saline than it is?

Answer: Chemical substances are being removed from ocean water at the same time they are being added. Because the processes of removal are equal to the combined input processes, the composition of seawater remains essentially constant instead of becoming more and more saline.

2. What geologic features might indicate that a coastline had undergone submergence or emergence in the recent past?

Answer: Submergence is indicated by features like former beaches, sand dunes, and other coastal landscape features now submerged on the inner continental shelf. Emergence is indicated by coastal land forms such as coral reefs or beaches occurring above current sea level.

3. Draw three neat, well-labelled diagrams illustrating the pycnocline, the halocline, and the thermocline, and their relationship to the surface zone and deep zone.

Answer: (See Fig. 8.7 in the text.)

4. How do we know that liquid water has been present on the Earth for at least 3.95 billion years?

Answer: The Earth's oldest rocks, which are 3.95 billion years old, include sedimentary strata that were deposited by water.

5. What are the most important factors that affect the salinity of seawater? In what way does each of these factors affect the salinity of the water?

Answer: They are (1) evaporation (which removes water and leaves the remaining water saltier), (2) precipitation (which adds fresh water, thereby diluting the seawater and making it less salty), (3) inflow of fresh (river) water (which makes the seawater less salty), and (4) the freezing and melting of sea ice (when seawater freezes, salts are excluded from the ice, leaving the unfrozen seawater saltier).

6. What is a tsunami? Why are tsunami hazardous?

Answer: A tsunami, or seismic sea wave, is a very long-wavelength (up to 200 km, or 124 mi) water wave. They are caused by large earthquakes or other brief, large-scale disturbances of the ocean floor, such as landslides or volcanic eruptions. Tsunami are hazardous because they can travel up to 950 km/h (590 mi/h), and can pile up rapidly to water heights of 30 m (100 ft) or more as it moves into shallow water along an exposed coast.

7. Why is it unlikely that tidal power will ever be a significant contributor to the global energy supply?

Answer: The harnessing of tidal power requires a particular type of setting, specifically, a narrow, restricted bay with a large tidal range. There is a limited number of suitable locations on the Earth; even if all of them were exploited, the total recoverable energy would be equivalent to only about a tenth that annually obtained from oil. Also, unlike hydroelectric power, the power supply from tides is erratic because it can only be exploited twice a day.

VI. Longer-Answer Questions, Essays & Critical Thinking Questions: Answers are not provided for these questions (because each student will formulate his or her answer differently), but page numbers for text references are given at the end of each question.

1. What are the main sources of the ions that make ocean water saline? (p. 199-200)

2. What factors cause sea levels to rise and fall on long time scales? What happens to the world's coastlines when sea levels rise or fall? (p. 219-220)

3. Summarize your understanding of the El Niño/Southern Oscillation phenomenon. How have corals helped to provide a record of past El Niño events? (p. 207-209)

4. Describe how surface waves change as they travel from deep water through shallow water to shore. A neat, well-labelled diagram would be an appropriate addition to your answer. (p. 213-214)

5. Explain how the Coriolis effect influences ocean circulation. (p. 203-205)

6. Describe how geostrophic flow can trap a large lens of water in the middle of a gyre. (p. 209)

7. Explain why El Niño events have an adverse effect on fishing off the coast of Peru. (p. 207)

CHAPTER 9: Water on the Land: Surface Streams and Groundwater

---

I. Multiple Choice Questions

1. Recharge area refers to an area

x   a. where precipitation infiltrates and flows to join an aquifer.
    b. where groundwater feeds a spring or stream.
    c. where pollution mixes with groundwater.
    d. over which sewage-contaminated groundwater becomes purified by seeping through permeable fine sands.

2.   Which one of the following does not belong with the others?

        a.   rolling
x   b.   oscillating
        c.   sliding
        d.   saltation

3.   The average grain size of a stream's load tends to _____ downstream.

        a.   increase
x   b.   decrease
        c.   remain more or less the same

4.   Which one of the following does not belong with the others?

x   a.   suspension
        b.   rolling
        c.   sliding
        d.   saltation

5.   Which one of the following does not influence water quality?

        a.   natural dissolved substances
        b.   agricultural pollutants
        c.   industrial pollutants
x   d.   All of the above have an influence on water quality.

6.   Depletion of an aquifer can be caused by

        a.   crustal subsidence.
        b.   drilling a well in the vicinity of an Artesian aquifer.
        c.   drilling into a confined aquifer.
x   d.   withdrawing water at greater than the rate of recharge.

7.   Stream discharge refers to

x   a.   the volume of water flowing past a point during a given period of time.
        b.   the amount of sediment carried by the stream.
        c.   the amount of water drained by a given drainage basin or discharge system.
        d.   the velocity of flow in a river.

8.   The phrase "cone of depression" refers to

      a.   a region of land surrounded by divides and drained by one stream and its tributaries.

x   b.   a depression in the water table caused by withdrawal of water at rates greater than those at which the water can be replenished by natural groundwater flow.

      c.   the detachment of soil and broken rock and its subsequent downslope movement in a cone-shaped or fan-shaped mass.

      d.   a large, basin-shaped volcanic depression, typically originating through volcanic explosion and/or collapse.

9.   Porosity in rocks and regolith is defined as

      a.   interconnections among the pores between grains.

x   b.   the proportion of pore space to total volume.

      c.   the ability to absorb and transmit water.

      d.   the degree of lithification.

10.   The hydrologic cycle is driven by

x   a.   energy from the sun.

      b.   precipitation.

      c.   groundwater flow.

      d.   energy from the Earth's interior.

11.   The hydrologic cycle maintains a mass balance. This means that

      a.   the majority of water in the cycle is held in reservoirs, particularly the oceans.

x   b.   the total amount of water in the system is essentially fixed, although the amount held in any given reservoir during a given period of time may vary considerably.

      c.   the amount or mass of water held at any one time in the oceans is approximately matched by the amount which occurs in the form of groundwater.

      d.   the surface area of one drainage basin approximately matches that of the adjacent basin.

12.   A good aquifer is typically

      a.   porous but not permeable.

      b.   permeable but not porous.

x   c.   porous and permeable.

      d.   dependent on grain size.

13.   The most important feature of a rock suitable for the containment of highly toxic wastes is that it must be

x   a.   isolated from groundwater.
      b.   thick.
      c.   porous.
      d.   permeable.

14.   Particles which are carried in a jumping or bouncing motion by water are said to be in

      a.   traction.
x   b.   saltation.
      c.   solution.
      d.   suspension.

15.   As stream discharge increases which of the following may also increase?

      a.   width of channel
      b.   depth of channel
      c.   velocity of flow
x   d.   All of the above are true.

16.   A type of well in which the water rises above the surface under its own pressure is called a(an) _____ well.

      a.   injection
      b.   perched
      c.   confined
x   d.   artesian

17.   Excessive withdrawal of groundwater from an aquifer results in

      a.   excessive recharge.
      b.   the formation of an injection well.
x   c.   the formation of a cone of depression.
      d.   bulging up of the surface.

18. The zones of aeration and saturation are separated by

      a.   a cone of depression.
x   b.   the water table.
      c.   the soil water layer.
      d.   an aquifer.

19. Porosity is mainly affected by

      a.   the size of particles.
      b.   the degree of sorting of particles.
      c.   the amount of cementing material present in pore spaces.
x   d.   All of the above are true.

20. Which one of the following statements is false?

      a.   Groundwater typically moves at rates between about half a meter per day to several meters per year.
      b.   Groundwater flow responds to gravity, in that it tends to move from areas where the water table is high toward areas where it is lowest.
x   c.   Groundwater is not present in the zone of aeration; by definition, the pore spaces in this zone are filled with air.
      d.   Sometimes groundwater is discharged into streams or lakes from beneath them.

II.   Fill-Ins

1. A(n) _____ encompasses the area supplying water to the stream system that drains it.

   (drainage basin)

2. The area of a drainage basin is closely related to the _____ and _____ of the stream that drains it.

   (length...annual discharge) or (size...discharge)

3. Stream load is the sum of _____ load, _____ , and _____ load.

   (bed...suspended...dissolved)

4.   A stream's bed load moves by _____ , _____ , and _____ .

     (rolling...sliding...saltation)

5.   The water table marks the boundary between the _____ and the _____ .

     (zone of aeration...saturated zone)

6.   A well into which groundwater flows under hydraulic pressure is called a(n) _____ well.

     (artesian)

7.   A confined aquifer is bounded by bodies of _____ rock adjacent to an aquifer.

     (impermeable) or (less permeable)

8.   The accumulation of _____ behind a dam reduces the useful life of a reservoir.

     (sediment)

9.   _____ is the portion of precipitation that runs off over the land surface.

     (Runoff)

10. When water from precipitation moves downslope in broad, thin sheets it is referred to as _____ .

     (overland flow)

11. The line that separates adjacent drainage basins is called a(n) _____ .

     (divide)

12. A meander that is cut off when the stream bypasses the channel loop and cuts straight through from upstream to downstream becomes a(n) _____ .

     (oxbow lake)

13. The _____ is the vertical distance that a stream channel descends over the horizontal distance between two points along its course.

(gradient)

14. A(n) _____ occurs when a stream's discharge becomes so great that it exceed the capacity of the channel, and water overflows the stream banks.

(flood)

15. The interception and diversion of a stream by another stream that is expanding its basin in the headward direction is called _____ .

(stream capture)

16. A stream that joins a larger stream is called a(n) _____ .

(tributary)

III. Definitions

1. alluvium: sediment deposited by streams in nonmarine environments.

2. aquifer: a body of permeable rock or regolith saturated with water and through which groundwater moves.

3. artesian aquifer: an aquifer in which water is under hydraulic pressure.

4. bed load: coarse particles that move along the bottom of a stream channel.

5. braided stream: a channel system consisting of a tangled network of two or more smaller branching and reuniting channels that are separated by islands or bars.

6. channel: the passageway in which a stream flows.

7. cone of depression: a conical depression in the water table immediately surrounding a well.

8. confined aquifer: an aquifer bounded by impermeable or less permeable rock or regolith units.

9.   discharge: the quantity of water that passes a given point in a stream channel per unit time.

10. discharge area: area where subsurface water is discharged to streams or to bodies of surface water.

11. dissolved load: matter dissolved in stream water.

12. divide: the line that separates adjacent drainage basins.

13. drainage basin: the total area that contributes water to a stream.

14. gradient: a measure of the vertical drop over a given horizontal distance.

15. groundwater: all the water contained in the spaces within bedrock and regolith.

16. load: the material that is moved or carried by a natural transporting agent, such as a stream, the wind, a glacier, or waves, tides, and current.

17. meander: a looplike bend of a stream channel.

18. permeability: a measure of how easily a solid allows a fluid to pass through it.

19. porosity: the proportion (in percent) of the total volume of a given body of bedrock or regolith that consists of pore spaces.

20. recharge: the addition of water to the saturated zone of a groundwater system.

21. recharge area: area where water is added to the saturated zone.

22. runoff: the fraction of precipitation that flows over the land surface.

23. saltation: the progressive forward movement of a sediment particle in a series of short intermittent jumps along arcing paths.

24. saturated zone: the groundwater zone in which all openings are filled with water.

25. stream: a body of water that carries detrital particles and dissolved substances and flows down a slope in a definite channel.

26. suspended load: fine particles suspended in a stream.

191

27. tributary: a stream that joins a larger stream.

28. unconfined aquifer: an aquifer with an upper surface that coincides with the water table.

29. water table: the upper surface of the saturated zone of groundwater.

30. zone of aeration: the groundwater zone in which open spaces in regolith or bedrock are filled mainly with air.

IV.   True-False Questions

1. Straight stream channels are rare. (T)

2. Water is not present in the zone of aeration; by definition, the pore spaces are filled with air. (F)

3. Groundwater is replenished in recharge areas. (T)

4. The drainage basin of the Mississippi River encompasses an area that exceeds 40 percent of the area of the contiguous United States. (T)

5. When a stream enlarges its channel through erosion, a greater discharge can be accommodated in a larger channel and by faster flow. (T)

6. Braided stream patterns typically form when a stream is unable to transport all the available load, or when discharge is highly variable. (T)

7. The bed load generally accounts for 50 to 60 percent of the total sediment load of most streams. (F)

8. Clear water generally carries no suspended load. (F)

9. The size of the particles a stream can transport is related mainly to the velocity of the water. (T)

10. Approximately 40% of the water in the hydrosphere is groundwater. (F)

11. Permeability is the proportion of the total volume of a body of bedrock or regolith that consists of open spaces. (F)

12. About 10% of the groundwater used for irrigation in the United States is obtained from the High Plains aquifer. (F)

13. The velocity of water flowing in a river's channel tends to be essentially the same from one bank to the other. (F)

14. A stream that joins a larger stream is called a meander. (F)

V.   Short-Answer Questions

1.   What is an artesian well?

Answer: An artesian well is a water well drilled into an artesian aquifer. In such a well, water will rise to the height of the water table in its recharge area; if the top of the well is lower than this in altitude, water will flow freely out at the surface, without pumping.

2.   What is an artesian spring?

Answer: An artesian spring is a freely flowing spring, supplied by an artesian aquifer (an aquifer in which the level of the water table in the recharge area is higher than the ground surface above the aquifer, and water is therefore under hydraulic pressure).

3.   What is hard water? What is soft water?

Answer: Hard water is water that is rich in calcium and magnesium bicarbonates that have been dissolved from the local carbonate bedrock. Typically, soap does not lather well in hard water. Hard water can also lead to the deposition of scaly crusts in pipes, which may restrict water flow. Soft water contains little dissolved matter and, in particular, no appreciable calcium.

4.   What do we mean when we use the expression "mining groundwater"?

Answer: Groundwater is, in principal, renewable. However, when groundwater is withdrawn at rates much higher than the natural rate of recharge, aquifers can become depleted. In some cases it make take so long to replenish a depleted aquifer (hundreds or even thousands of years) that the resource has essentially lost. In this case, the resource is essentially nonrenewable, and when it is removed from the ground it is tantamount to "mining" the resource.

5.   What is the relationship between discharge, velocity, and channel shape?

Answer: Discharge = Cross-sectional area of channel × Average velocity

6.   What is a point bar? Include a neat, well-labelled diagram showing where point bars tend to form in meandering streams.

Answer: Point bars form along the inner side of a meander loop, where water is shallow and velocity is low. Coarse sediment tends to accumulate in these regions, causing the build-up of gravelly alluvium that is referred to as a point bar. For example, a point bar would tend to form at position number 5 or across the channel from position number 2 on Figure 9.5 in the text.

7.   What is saltation? Include a neat, well-labelled diagram to illustrate your answer.

Answer: Saltation involves the progressive forward movement of a particle in short, intermittent jumps along arcuate paths. It is a type of movement that is intermediate between suspension and rolling or sliding. Current must be sufficiently turbulent to lift the particles in order for saltation to continue. (See Fig. 9.9 in the text.)

8.   What are the five main factors that control a stream's behavior?

Answer: (1) average width and depth of the channel; (2) channel gradient; (3) average velocity of the water; (4) discharge; (5) sediment load

9.   What factors can contribute to the formation of a braided stream pattern?

Answer: Braided stream patterns tend to form where a stream is unable to handle all of the available discharge. Therefore, highly variable discharge and easily erodible banks that can supply abundant sediment load to the stream would tend to contribute to the formation of braided stream patterns.

VI.   Longer-Answer Questions, Essays & Critical Thinking Questions: Answers are not provided for these questions (because each student will formulate his or her answer differently), but page numbers for text references are given at the end of each question.

1.   Given what you know about the relationship between stream discharge, velocity, and channel width, why do you think stream velocities usually increase downstream despite a decrease in stream gradient? (p. 227-228)

2. Describe some of the unexpected environmental impacts that have been caused by the construction of the Aswan Dam. (p. 225-226, 233, 242)

3. Discuss the main types of human impacts on rivers. (p. 242-243)

4. Discuss the main types of human impacts on groundwater. (p. 243-245).

5. What is the difference between the bed load, suspended load, and dissolved load of a stream? (p. 231-232)

6. With respect to groundwater and surface water, what do you think would be the characteristics of a safe site for the disposal of toxic or nuclear wastes? (p. 245-246)

CHAPTER 10: The World of Snow and Ice

I. Multiple Choice Questions

1. The snowline is

x   a.   the lower limit of perennial snow.
    b.   the line along which ablation is balanced by accumulation in a glacier.
    c.   the terminus of a glacier.
    d.   the point on a glacier where net mass loss equals net mass gain.

2. Which one of the following does not belong with the others?

    a.   fjord glacier
x   b.   snowline glacier
    c.   cirque glacier
    d.   valley glacier

3. Which one of the following does not belong with the others?

    a.   ice caps
    b.   ice sheets
    c.   ice shelves
x   d.   ice bergs

4.   In the context of sea ice, a lead is

x   a.   a long, linear opening caused by diverging movement.
    b.   a pressure ridge formed when the shifting ice converges and shears.
    c.   a seasonal ice zone.
    d.   like the terminus of a glacier.

5.   The depth of a permafrost layer depends on

    a.   the average ambient air temperature.
    b.   how long the ground has remained continuously frozen.
    c.   the rate at which heat flows upward from the Earth's interior.
x   d.   All of the above are true.

6.   When, over a period of years, a glacier gains more mass than it loses, the likely result will be that

    a.   the terminus of the glacier will advance.
    b.   the volume of the glacier will increase.
    c.   the glacier will grow.
x   d.   All of the above are true.

7.   A polynya is

    a.   created when pressure ridges form in sea ice.
x   b.   an area of open water enclosed by sea ice.
    c.   a mass of deformed ice, like the keel of a boat, which may be up to five times as thick as the overlying ridge of sea ice.
    d.   the first mass of crystals to form when sea water begins to freeze.

8.   In permafrost terrain, a thin surface layer of ground that thaws in summer and refreezes in winter is known as a(n)

    a.   lead.
x   b.   active layer.
    c.   polynya.
    d.   terminus.

9.   The maximum reported depth of permafrost is about _____ meters.

      a.   15
      b.   150
x   c.   1500
      d.   15,000

10. Scientists learn about _____ from ice cores taken from the Greenland and Antarctic ice sheets.

      a.   past air temperatures
      b.   the past composition of local vegetation near a glacier
      c.   the timing of major volcanic eruptions
x   d.   All of the above are true.

11. When the cover of vegetation on a permafrost landscape is disturbed, _____ can begin.

      a.   construction
x   b.   melting
      c.   water circulation
      d.   oil extraction

12. The progressive breaking off of icebergs from a glacier that terminates in deep water is called

x   a.   calving.
      b.   polynya.
      c.   ablation.
      d.   surging.

13. A cirque is

      a.   a deep, gaping fissure in the upper surface of a glacier.
x   b.   a bowl-shaped depression on a mountainside, produced by glacial erosion.
      c.   an accumulation of drift deposited beneath or at the margin of a glacier.
      d.   an unusually rapid movement of a glacier.

14. The surface reflectivity of materials on a planetary surface is called the

     a.   isostasy.
     b.   geothermal gradient.
x   c.   albedo.
     d.   luminosity.

15. A moraine is

x   a.   a bowl-shaped depression on a mountainside, produced by glacial erosion.
     b.   a deep, gaping fissure in the upper surface of a glacier.
     c.   an accumulation of drift deposited beneath or at the margin of a glacier.
     d.   an accumulation of sediment, soil, or bedrock that remains continuously at a temperature below 0°C for an extended time.

16. The formation of a glacier requires

     a.   high altitudes and steep slopes.
x   b.   conditions in which the amount of snow falling each winter is greater than the amount that melts during the following summer.
     c.   extremely cold ambient air temperatures.
     d.   All of the above are true.

17. The land area beyond the limit of glacier, where low temperature and frost action are important factors in determining landscape characteristics, is called the

     a.   moraine.
x   b.   periglacial zone.
     c.   permafrost.
     d.   active layer.

18. Glaciers

x   a.   consist largely of recrystallized snow.
     b.   are frozen in place.
     c.   advance and retreat each year in response to seasonal changes.
     d.   All of the above are true.

19. The altitude of the snowline is affected by _____ and _____ .

  a. winter snowfall...summer temperature
  b. ocean moisture sources...topography
  c. precipitation...air temperature
 x d. All of the above are true.

20. An accumulation of drift deposited beneath or at the margin of a glacier is called a(n)

 x a. moraine.
  b. active layer.
  c. rockfall.
  d. cirque.

II. Fill-Ins

1. The altitude of the snowline is controlled mainly by _____ and _____ .

 (precipitation...summer temperature)

2. The mass balance of a glacier is the sum of _____ and _____ .

 (ablation...accumulation)

3. The _____ of a glacier separates the accumulation area from the ablation area, and marks the level on the glacier where net gain is balanced by net loss.

 (equilibrium line)

4. Temperate glaciers move as a result of _____ and _____ .

 (internal flow...basal sliding)

5. The part of the Earth's surface that remains perennially frozen is called the _____ .

 (cryosphere)

6.   A(n) _____ involves extremely rapid flow in a glacier, probably related to excessive amounts of water at the base.

     (surge)

7.   A fjord glacier with its base below sea level will retreat by the process of _____ if its terminus becomes ungrounded and recedes into deep water.

     (calving)

8.   About _____ percent of the Earth's land surface is covered by glaciers, while perennially frozen land constitutes an additional _____ percent.

     (10...20)

9.   The first ice crystals to form when sea ice freezes are small platelets and needles up to 3 or 4 mm (0.1 or 0.2 in) in diameter, which are collectively called _____ .

     (frazil ice)

10. A long, linear opening caused by stresses resulting from diverging movement in thin sea ice is called a(n) _____ .

     (lead)

III.   Definitions

1.   ablation: the loss of mass from a glacier.

2.   accumulation: the addition of mass to a glacier.

3.   albedo: the reflectivity of the surface of a planet.

4.   calving: the progressive breaking off of icebergs from a glacier that terminates in deep water.

5.   cirque: a bowl-shaped hollow on a mountainside, open downstream, bounded upstream by a steep slope (headwall), and excavated mainly by frost wedging and by glacial abrasion and plucking.

6. crevasse: a deep, gaping fissure in the upper surface of a glacier.

7. cryosphere: the part of the Earth's surface that remains perennially frozen.

8. equilibrium line: a line that marks the level on a glacier where net mass loss equals net gain.

9. fjord (fiord): a deep, glacially carved valley submerged by the sea.

10. glacier: a permanent body of ice, consisting largely of recrystallized snow, that shows evidence of downslope or outward movement, due to the stress of its own weight.

11. glacier ice: snow that gradually becomes denser and denser until it is no longer permeable to air.

12. lead (in sea ice): a linear opening in thin ice cover caused by stresses resulting form the diverging movement of the ice cover.

13. mass balance (of a glacier): the sum of the accumulation and ablation on a glacier during a year.

14. moraine: an accumulation of drift deposited beneath or at the margin of a glacier and having a surface form that is unrelated to the underlying bedrock.

15. periglacial: a land area beyond the limit of glaciers where low temperature and frost action are important factors in determining landscape characteristics.

16. permafrost: sediment, soil, or bedrock that remains continuously at a temperature below 0°C for an extended time.

17. polar glacier: a glacier in which the ice is below the pressure melting point throughout, and the ice is frozen to its bed.

18. pressure melting point: the temperature at which ice can melt at a given pressure.

19. sea ice: a thin veneer of ice at the ocean surface in the polar latitudes; accounts for approximately two-thirds of the Earth's permanent ice cover.

20. snowline: the lower limit of perennial snow.

21. surge: an unusually rapid movement of a glacier marked by dramatic changes in glacier flow and form.

22. temperate glacier: a glacier in which the ice is at the pressure-melting point and water and ice coexist in equilibrium.

IV. True-False Questions

1. Glaciers constitute the bulk of the ice in the cryosphere. (T)

2. The cryosphere consists of sea ice and glaciers. (F)

3. Rates of flow in polar glaciers are generally faster than in temperate glaciers. (F)

4. Icebergs in the Arctic Ocean are less numerous but larger, on average, than icebergs around Antarctica. (F)

5. The surface areas of the polar ice caps fluctuate seasonally, but remain more or less the same over longer periods of geologic time. (F)

6. Nearly a third of the Earth's land surface area is perennially frozen and thus belongs to the cryosphere. (T)

7. The snowline is defined by the lower boundary of the snow-covered zone at the end of the summer. (T)

8. Glacial surges are generally caused by unusually warm periods. (F)

9. Glaciers consist largely of recrystallized snow. (T)

10. Climatic conditions near the equator are too warm for glaciers to be able to form. (F)

11. Almost all high-mountain glaciers have shrunk substantially in recent decades. (T)

12. Glaciers occur near polar regions, not near the equator. (F)

V.   Short-Answer Questions

1.   Describe the changes that take place in snow as it turns into glacier ice and becomes buried deep within the glacier. Include a neat, well-labelled diagram to illustrate your answer.

Answer: (See Fig. 10.9 in the text.) Newly fallen snow is very porous and permeable to air. Snow that survives a year or more gradually becomes denser and denser until it is no longer permeable to air, at which point it becomes glacier ice. Further changes take place as the ice becomes buried deeper and deeper within the glacier. Increasing pressure causes initially small grains of glacier ice to grow until, near the base of the ice sheet, they may reach a diameter of 1 cm (0.4 in) or more.

2.   Why doesn't the advance or retreat of a glacier terminus give an accurate picture of changing climatic conditions?

Answer: A lag time occurs between a climatic change and the response of the glacier terminus to that change. The lag reflects the time it takes for the effects of an increase or a decrease in accumulation above the equilibrium line to be transferred through the slowly moving ice to the glacier terminus. The length of the lag depends both on the size of a glacier and on the way the ice moves; the lag will be longer for large glaciers than for small ones and longer for polar glaciers than for temperate one.

3.   How come some glaciers in a region may be advancing while others in the same region are retreating or remaining stationary?

Answer: The main reason is that the time it takes for the terminus of a glacier to respond to climatic changes in a given region (the lag time) depends partially on the size of the glacier. Specifically, the lag time will be longer for large glaciers than for small ones. This means that small glaciers may start retreating in response to a warm period before moderate-sized or large glaciers, which may have lag times of several years to a decade or more. Some events, such as rockfalls, may also cause glaciers to retreat or advance at different rates from other glaciers in the same climatic environment.

4.   What is the difference between a temperate glacier and a polar glacier?

Answer: A temperate glacier is also called a "warm" glacier; ice is at the pressure melting point, and water exists at the base of the glacier. A polar glacier is also called a "cold" glacier; ice is below the pressure melting point and is frozen to the rock on which it rests.

5.   Explain how the terminus of a fjord glacier can become unstable and initiate rapid calving.

Answer: Although the base of a fjord glacier may lie far below sea level along much of its length, its terminus can remain stable as long as it is resting against a shoal or shallow submarine ridge. However, it the terminus retreats off the shoal, water will replace the space that had been occupied by ice, and the glacier will terminate in water and calving can occur. Because a fjord glacier increase in thickness in the upfjord direction, the water will become progressively deeper as the calving terminus retreats. The deepening water leads to faster retreat because the greater the water depth, the faster the calving rate. Once started, calving will continue rapidly and irreversibly until the glacier front has receded into water too shallow for calving to occur.

VI.   Longer-Answer Questions, Essays & Critical Thinking Questions: Answers are not provided for these questions (because each student will formulate his or her answer differently), but page numbers for text references are given at the end of each question.

1.   What are some of the technical problems associated with the proposal to tow huge icebergs from Antarctica to water-scarce regions such as the Middle East? (p. 251)

2.   Describe in some detail how ice coring has been used to provide scientists with evidence concerning past climatic changes and surface conditions on our planet. (p. 265, 272-273)

3.   Describe the process of internal flow in a glacier. Include a neat, well-labelled diagram to illustrate the effects of internal flow on ice crystals. (p. 261; Fig. 10.14)

4.   Describe the process of sea ice formation. (p. 265)

5.   Compare and contrast the major characteristics of the Arctic and Antarctic ice sheets. (p. 266)

6.   How does the albedo of sea ice influence global climate? What changes might you expect to occur in Arctic sea ice during a period of climatic warming? (p. 268)

CHAPTER 11: The Changing Face of the Land

I.   Multiple Choice Questions

1.   Which one of the following does not belong with the others?

    a.   alluvial fan
x   b.   sinkhole
    c.   delta
    d.   sediment deposition

2.   Which one of the following does not belong with the others?

    a.   karst topography
    b.   dissolution
    c.   sinkhole
x   d.   alluvial fan

3.   Which one of the following does not belong with the others?

    a.   striations
    b.   rock flour
    c.   glacial grooves
x   d.   deltas

4.   The type of drainage pattern developed over a flat area of uniform rocks is a _____ pattern.

    a.   trellis
    b.   rectangular
    c.   radial
x   d.   dendritic

5.   Which one of the following does not belong with the others?

x   a.   dune
      b.   cirque
      c.   fjord
      d.   drumlin

6.   Which one of the following does not belong with the others?

      a.   dune
      b.   loess
      c.   barchan
x   d.   atoll

7.   Mass wasting is primarily a function of

x   a.   gravity.
      b.   rainfall.
      c.   the nature of surface materials.
      d.   vegetative cover.
      e.   All of the above are true.

8.   Which one of the following does not belong with the others?

      a.   fringing reef
      b.   atoll
x   c.   barrier island
      d.   barrier reef

9.   As an island subsides, a(n) _____ reef will be transformed into a(n) _____ reef.

x   a.   fringing...barrier
      b.   atoll...fringing
      c.   barrier...fringing
      d.   island...atoll

10. Which one of the following can be both a downslope driving force and a resisting or stabilizing force in mass-wasting processes under different conditions?

     a.   slope
     b.   gravity
     c.   earthquakes
x   d.   water

11. Which one of the following does not belong with the others?

     a.   moraine
x   b.   loess
     c.   outwash
     d.   kettle lake

12. Soil is

     a.   weathered regolith.
x   b.   regolith which can support plants.
     c.   a type of Earth material which does not contain minerals.
     d.   All of the above.

13. Which one of the following does not belong with the others?

     a.   barrier island
     b.   beach
     c.   spit
x   d.   atoll

14. Natural levees along a stream channel mark

     a.   the position of the annual flood.
x   b.   the channel margins.
     c.   the edges of abandoned terraces.
     d.   the limit of the river's floodplain.

15. The "A" soil horizon is

x   a.   a zone from which soluble minerals have been removed.
       b.   a zone where soluble minerals accumulate.
       c.   a zone dominated by decomposing organic matter.
       d.   a zone in which oxidation occurs.

16. Soil formation is a function of

       a.   climate and vegetation cover.
       b.   soil organisms and regolith composition.
       c.   topography and time.
x   d.   All of the above are true.

17. The rock type most easily affected by dissolution is

       a.   shale.
x   b.   carbonate.
       c.   granite.
       d.   basalt.

18. The characteristics of a delta are determined by

       a.   the stream's discharge.
       b.   the character and volume of the sediment load.
       c.   the shape of the adjacent bedrock coastline and offshore topography.
x   d.   All of the above are true.

19. Which one of the following statements is false?

       a.   Air cannot move as large a particle as water can flowing at the same velocity.
       b.   In most regions, wind speed rarely exceeds 50 km/h (30 mi/h).
x   c.   Wind is an important agent of erosion wherever it is strong and persistent.
       d.   The density of air at sea level is far less than that of water.

20. The shapes of sand dunes depend on

    a.   wind strength and direction.
    b.   local moisture conditions.
    c.   local vegetation.
x   d.   All of the above are true.

II.   Fill-Ins

1.   _____ is weathered regolith capable of supporting plants.

    (Soil)

2.   The principal agents that erode the land and transfer sediment toward the ocean basins are _____ , _____ , and _____ .

    (water...ice...wind)

3.   The decomposition of rocks and minerals by chemical reactions with substances in water or air is called _____ .

    (chemical weathering)

4.   The principal agent of chemical erosion is a weak solution of _____ , formed as falling rainwater dissolves small quantities of atmospheric carbon dioxide.

    (carbonic acid) or (H_2CO_3)

5.   _____ is the downslope movement of regolith under the pull of gravity.

    (Mass-wasting)

6.   A closed basin created by the melting away of a mass of underlying glacier ice is referred to as a(n) _____ .

    (kettle)

7. An end moraine built at the terminus of a glacier is called a(n) _____ moraine.

    (terminal)

8. An end moraine built along the side of a mountain glacier is called a(n) _____ moraine.

    (lateral)

9. The three principal types of reefs are _____ , _____ , and _____ .

    (fringing reef...barrier reef...atoll)

10. Shoreline features which occur above present sea level is indicative of _____ , a lowering of the water level relative to the land.

    (emergence)

III. Definitions

1. alluvial fan: a fan-shaped body of alluvium typically built where a stream leaves a steep mountain valley.

2. beach: wave-washed sediment along a coast, extending throughout the surf zone.

3. chemical weathering: the decomposition of rocks through chemical reactions such as hydration and oxidation.

4. delta: a body of sediment deposited by a stream where it flows into standing water.

5. denudation: the sum of the weathering, mass-wasting, and erosional processes that result in the progressive lowering of the Earth's surface.

6. dissolution: the chemical weathering process whereby minerals and rock material pass directly into solution.

7. dune: a mound or ridge of sand deposited by wind.

8. emergence: an increase in the area of land exposed above sea level resulting form uplift of the land and/or fall of sea level.

9. end moraine: a ridgelike accumulation of drift deposited along the margin of a glacier.

10. floodplain: the part of any stream valley that is inundated during floods.

11. karst topography: an assemblage of topographic forms resulting from dissolution of carbonate bedrock and consisting primarily of closely spaced sinks.

12. landslide: any perceptible downslope movement of a mass of bedrock or regolith, or a mixture of the two.

13. loess: wind-deposited silt, sometimes accompanied by some clay and fine sand.

14. mass-wasting: the movement of regolith downslope by gravity without the aid of a transporting medium.

15. physical weathering: the disintegration (physical breakup) of rocks.

16. sand seas: vast tract of shifting sand.

17. sinkhole: a large solution cavity open to the sky.

18. soil: the part of the regolith that can support rooted plants.

19. soil horizon: the subhorizontal weathered zones formed as a soil develops.

20. soil profile: a vertical section through a soil that displays its component horizons.

21. striations: subparallel scratches inscribed on a clast or bedrock surface by rock debris embedded in the base of a glacier.

22. submergence: a rise of water level relative to the land so that areas formerly dry are inundated.

23. terrace: an abandoned floodplain formed when a stream flowed at a level above the level of its present channel and floodplain.

24. topographic relief: the difference in altitude between the highest and lowest points on a landscape.

25. weathering: the chemical alteration and mechanical breakdown of rock materials during exposure to air, moisture, and organic matter.

IV. True-False Questions

1. Physical and chemical weathering processes generally operate separately. (F)

2. Most beach-forming sediment is derived from erosion of adjacent cliffs or older beach deposits. (F)

3. Since water does not exist on Mars, the erosional features observed there by the Mariner 9 spacecraft must have formed by wind erosion. (F)

4. The zone of weathering extends from the ground surface downward to whatever depth air and water are able to penetrate. (T)

5. Quartz is a mineral that is particularly resistant to chemical weathering. (T)

6. Fire can be an effective agent of weathering. (T)

7. Carbonate rocks are particularly susceptible to chemical weathering by dissolution. (T)

8. Karst topography is an example of glacially sculpted terrain. (F)

9. Drumlins are parallel ridges of rock or glacially deposited regolith, which are elongated parallel to the direction of glacial flow. (T)

10. Wind erosion on a large scale takes place only where little or no vegetation exists and where loose rock particles are fine enough to be picked up by the wind. (T)

11. Nearly all coasts have experienced recent submergence. (T)

12. Worldwide, productive agricultural soil is eroding at a rate of about 7 percent each decade. (T)

V. Short-Answer Questions

1. List five different types of events or activities that commonly cause landslides.

Answer: (1) earthquakes; (2) prolonged or heavy rains; (3) volcanic eruptions; (4) human modifications of slopes (such as oversteepening due to road construction); (5) undercutting of slopes by streams or surf.

2. How does physical weathering differ from chemical weathering?

Answer: In physical weathering, the fragments of regolith are identical to the adjacent bedrock, indicating that the fragments have undergone disintegration (physical breakup) without changing their chemical compositions or mineralogies. In chemical weathering, by contrast, minerals are transformed into new chemical combinations through interactions between rocks and water, air, or chemicals in the water or air.

3. How are caves and sinkholes different? How are they the same?

Answer: Caves and sinkholes are both cavities that form when circulating groundwater slowly dissolves carbonate rock. In contrast to a cave, a sinkhole is a dissolution cavity that is open to the sky. Some sinkholes are caves whose roofs have collapsed; others are formed at the surface.

4. What is a continental divide?

Answer: All continents (except Antarctica) can be divided into large regions in which major through-flowing streams enter one of the world's major oceans. The line separating any two such regions is called a continental divide.

5. Describe the process of formation of alluvial fans. Where do they occur most commonly?

Answer: Alluvial fans are common along the base of most arid and semi-arid mountain ranges. A large, swift stream flowing down a steep mountain valley can transport an abundant load of coarse sediment, but on leaving the valley the stream loses energy, usually because of a change in gradient, velocity, or discharge. Its transporting power therefore decreases, and it deposits part of its sediment load. No longer constrained by valley walls, the stream shifts laterally back and forth across more gentle terrain. The result is a fan-shaped body of alluvium that spreads out along the base of the upland.

6. Where does the organic matter in soils come from?

Answer: It is derived from the decay of dead plants and animals.

7. Match each description with the name of a type of landslide:

a. The free falling of detached bodies of bedrock from a cliff or steep slope.

i. slump

b. A slope failure in which a downward and outward rotational movement of rock or regolith occurs along a concave-up surface.

ii. rockslide

c. The sudden and rapid downslope movement of detached masses of bedrock across an inclined surface.

iii. mudflow

d. A flowing mass of predominantly fine-grained material that has enough water content to make it highly fluid.

iv. rockfall

Answer: a-iv; b-i; c-ii; d-iii

VI. Longer-Answer Questions, Essays & Critical Thinking Questions: Answers are not provided for these questions (because each student will formulate his or her answer differently), but page numbers for text references are given at the end of each question.

1. Why aren't soils the same everywhere? (p. 282-283)

2. Describe how underlying rock structures can control the drainage patterns that develop in a particular region. Give at least four examples of different stream patterns that something about the type and configuration of underlying rock formations. (p. 287-288, Fig. 11.10)

3. Describe four natural processes that are effective agents of physical weathering. (p. 281)

4. Why is soil erosion of particular concern today? (p. 283-284)

5. Discuss the role of water in mass-wasting. (p. 284-285)

6. Name at least four types of dunes and describe the conditions under which they form. (p. 298, Table 11.3)

7. How do the height and form of the land influence world and regional climates? (p. 305-306)

8. Discuss the different approaches used by geologists to estimate rates of uplift. (p. 303-304)

CHAPTER 12: Composition and Structure of the Atmosphere

I. Multiple Choice Questions

1. Which one of the following does not belong with the others?

   a. cirrus
   b. cirrocumulus
   c. cirrostratus
   x d. stratocumulus

2. The rising of air that occurs when two flowing air masses of different density meet is called

   a. density lifting.
   x b. frontal lifting.
   c. orographic lifting.
   d. convergence lifting.

3. The rising of air that occurs when flowing air is forced upward as a result of sloping terrain is called

   a. density lifting.
   b. frontal lifting.
   x c. orographic lifting.
   d. convergence lifting.

4. Clouds consist of

x a. water droplets and/or ice crystals.
   b. water vapor.
   c. aerosols.
   d. All of the above are true.

5. Which one of the following does not belong with the others?

x a. asthenosphere
   b. stratosphere
   c. troposphere
   d. thermosphere

6. Individual puffy, cauliflower-shaped clouds with flat bases are called _____ clouds.

x a. cumulus
   b. stratus
   c. nimbus
   d. cirrus

7. Fine, wispy, filamentous clouds which form high in the troposphere are called _____ clouds.

   a. cumulus
   b. stratus
   c. nimbus
x d. cirrus

8. The three major gases that account for 99.96 percent of dry, aerosol-free air are nitrogen, oxygen, and

   a. carbon dioxide.
   b. water vapor.
x c. argon.
   d. ozone.

9. The _____ is where most of the Earth's weather is generated, where most clouds form, and where rain and snow develop.

   x   a.   troposphere
         b.   stratosphere
         c.   mesosphere
         d.   thermosphere

10. The atmosphere extends out to an altitude of about _____ km, at which point it blends into the vacuum of space.

         a.   5
         b.   50
   x   c.   500
         d.   5000

11. Which one of the following is not one of the six changes of state that occur in the compound H_2O at or near the surface of the Earth?

         a.   sublimation
   x   b.   deposition
         c.   condensation
         d.   melting

12. The formation of a more ordered liquid from a less ordered gas is called

   x   a.   condensation.
         b.   sublimation.
         c.   evaporation.
         d.   precipitation.

13. Air pressure is measured with a device called a

         a.   Bergeron column.
         b.   gravimeter.
         c.   Torricelli.
   x   d.   barometer.

14. The mercury barometer was invented by

x a. Evangelista Torricelli.
   b. Blaise Pascal.
   c. Tor Bergeron.
   d. Alfred Wegener.

15. When air becomes saturated with water vapor,

   a. ice crystals precipitate.
   b. water condenses.
   c. supercooled water droplets form.
x d. Any of the above can occur, depending on ambient conditions.

16. An essential criterion for a habitable planet is

   a. the presence of oxygen in the atmosphere.
   b. the presence of water vapor.
   c. a comfortable ambient temperature.
x d. All of the above are true.

17. Air pressure decreases with altitude, but the decrease is not linear because of the

   a. Bergeron process.
   b. adiabatic lapse rate.
x c. compressibility of air.
   d. release of latent heat.

18. Scattering of sunlight in the atmosphere is caused by

   a. clouds.
   b. aerosols.
   c. gas molecules.
x d. All of the above are true.

19.   The sky appears blue because of

x   a.   Rayleigh scattering.
      b.   the Bergeron process.
      c.   the planet's albedo.
      d.   the greenhouse effect.

20.   Energy from the Sun that reaches the surface of the Earth is called

      a.   albedo.
      b.   solar energy.
      c.   the greenhouse effect.
x   d.   insolation.

II.   Fill-Ins

1.   The two energy sources that drive the atmosphere are _____ and _____ .

     (the Sun's heat...the Earth's rotation)

2.   _____ are tiny liquid droplets or tiny solid particles that are so small they remain suspended in the air.

     (Aerosols)

3.   In order to be habitable, a planet must have an oxygen level ranging from _____ percent above to _____ percent below the level found in today's air.

     (40...44)

4.   Energy from the Sun that reaches the surface of the Earth is called _____ .

     (insolation)

5.   The lowest of the Earth's four thermal layers is the _____ .

     (troposphere)

6. A(n) _____ is a helium-filled balloon used by meteorologists to carry recording instruments high into the atmosphere.

    (radiosonde)

7. The temperature at which the relative humidity reaches 100 percent and condensation begins is called the _____ .

    (dew point)

8. A(n) _____ process is a change in temperature that occurs without the addition or subtraction of heat from an external source.

    (adiabatic)

9. The way temperature changes with altitude in a rising or falling mass of air is called the _____ .

    (adiabatic lapse rate)

10. Two rare kinds of clouds, called _____ clouds and _____ , form in the stratosphere and consist entirely of tiny ice crystals.

    (nacreous...noctilucent)

11. As far as the weather is concerned, the three most important changes of state of H_2O are _____ , _____ , and _____ .

    (condensation...precipitation...evaporation)

III. Definitions

1. adiabatic lapse rate: the way temperature changes with altitude in rising or falling air.

2. adiabatic process: a process that happens without the addition or subtraction of heat from an external source.

3. aerosol: a tiny liquid droplet or tiny solid particle so small it remains suspended in air.

4. air: the invisible, odorless mixture of gases and suspended particles that surrounds the Earth.

5. barometer: a device that measures air pressure.

6. Bergeron process: the evaporation of supercooled water droplets in a cloud to release water vapor that is then deposited on ice crystals within the cloud, leading to precipitation.

7. climate: the average weather conditions of a place or area over a period of years.

8. cloud: visible aggregations of minute water droplets, tiny ice crystals, or both.

9. cold front: a front in which dense, cold air flows in and displaces warmer air by pushing it upward, producing clouds and possibly rain.

10. condensation: the formation of a more ordered liquid from a less ordered gas.

11. dew point: the temperature at which the relative humidity reaches 100 percent and condensation starts.

12. front: the boundary between air masses of different temperature and humidity, and therefore different density.

13. heat (heat energy): the energy a body has due to the motions of its atoms.

14. humidity: the amount of water vapor in the air.

15. insolation: the energy that reaches the surface of the Earth from the Sun.

16. latent heat: the amount of heat released or absorbed per gram during a change of state.

17. mesopause: the boundary between the mesosphere and the thermosphere.

18. mesosphere: one of the four thermal layers of the atmosphere, lying above the stratosphere.

19. occluded front: a front in which a cold air mass overtakes a warm air mass and meets another cold air mass, trapping the warm air mass in between.

20. relative humidity: the ratio of the vapor pressure in a sample of air to the saturation vapor pressure at the same temperature, expressed as a percentage.

21.   stratopause: the boundary between the stratosphere and the mesosphere.

22.   stratosphere: one of the four thermal layers of the atmosphere, lying above the troposphere and reaching a maximum of about 50 km.

23.   stratus clouds: sheets of cloud cover that form when air rises as a result of frontal lifting, reaches its level of condensation, and then spreads out laterally, covering the entire sky.

24.   temperature: a measure of the average kinetic energy of all the atoms in a body.

25.   thermosphere: one of the four thermal layers of the atmosphere, reaching out to about 500 km.

26.   tropopause: the boundary between the troposphere and the stratosphere.

27.   troposphere: one of the four thermal layers of the atmosphere, which extends from the surface of the Earth to variable altitudes of 10 to 16 km.

28.   warm front: a front in which warm, humid air advances over colder air, producing clouds and possibly rain.

29.   weather: the state of the atmosphere at a given time and place.

IV.   True-False Questions

1.   The Earth's first atmosphere is thought to have been lost about 4.5 billion years ago, almost as soon as the Earth had grown to its present size. (T)

2.   Heat energy is a measure of the average kinetic energy (energy of motion) of all the atoms in a body. (F)

3.   The oxygen content of the Earth's atmosphere has remained more or less constant since the stabilization of the atmosphere, about 3.95 billion years ago. (F)

4.   In the atmosphere, the amount of air per unit volume decreases with increasing altitude. (T)

5.   Three gases—nitrogen, oxygen, and argon—make up 99.96 percent of dry air by volume. (T)

6. In the thermosphere, the outermost of the Earth's four thermal layers, temperature increases with increasing altitude. (T)

7. Ninety-nine percent of the mass of the atmosphere lies below an altitude of 32 km (20 mi). (T)

8. Among naturally occurring compounds, H_2O is the only one with the ability to exist in three different physical states—solid, liquid, and gas—at the surface of the Earth. (T)

9. Warm air is denser than cold air. (F)

10. When a parcel of dry air rises and expands adiabatically, the temperature of the air increases. (F)

11. Clouds form when air rises and becomes saturated in response to adiabatic cooling. (T)

V. Short-Answer Questions

1. What is the difference between weather and climate?

Answer: Weather is the state of the atmosphere at a given time and place. Climate, on the other hand, is the average weather condition of a place over a period of years. Weather is a short-term event, whereas climate is a long-term one.

2. What is the difference between atmosphere and air?

Answer: An atmosphere is the gaseous envelope that surrounds a planet or any other celestial body. Air, by contrast, is the invisible, odorless mixture of gases and suspended particles that surrounds the Earth. Air is what makes up the Earth's atmosphere.

3. What is the difference between temperature and heat?

Answer: Heat or heat energy is the *total* kinetic energy (energy of motion) of all the atoms in a substance, whereas temperature is a measure of the *average* kinetic energy of all the atoms in a body.

4. Which five atmospheric gases are commonly called the "greenhouse gases"?

Answer: (1) carbon dioxide; (2) methane; (3) ozone; (4) nitrous oxide; (5) water vapor

5.   In what two ways has interaction with the biosphere altered the composition of the atmosphere?

Answer: (1) Through the process of photosynthesis, whereby plants combine CO_2 and H_2O to form organic matter and O_2, the biosphere added oxygen to the atmosphere; and (2) by removal of carbon from the atmosphere to form organic matter and limestone, the biosphere lowered the CO_2 content; as a result, the temperature declined.

6.   What are the five variables that meteorologists use to define the weather?

Answer: (1) temperature; (2) air pressure; (3) humidity; (4) cloudiness; (5) wind speed and direction

7.   Name at least four types of solid aerosols that commonly occur in the atmosphere.

Answer: (Any four of): tiny ice crystals, smoke particles from fires, sea-salt crystals from ocean spray, dust stirred up by winds, volcanic emissions, pollutants from industrial activities.

8.   Which two components of the Earth's atmosphere are highly variable from place to place on the Earth's surface and from time to time in the same place?

Answer: Aerosols and water vapor.

9.   What are the four things that can happen to sunlight when it enters the Earth's atmosphere?

Answer: It can (1) pass through unchanged and be absorbed by land or sea; (2) be reflected, unchanged, back into space; (3) be scattered by particles in the air; or (4) be absorbed by gases in the air.

VI.   Longer-Answer Questions, Essays & Critical Thinking Questions: Answers are not provided for these questions (because each student will formulate his or her answer differently), but page numbers for text references are given at the end of each question.

1.   Explain how greenhouse gases work to keep the surface of the Earth warm. (p. 315-315)

2.   Why is the sky blue? (p. 319-320)

3.   Explain how a simple mercury barometer works. (p. 320-321)

4.   Describe the four principal forces that lead to the upward movement of air. (p. 327-328)

5.   Describe the processes leading to the formation of snow and rain. (p. 326-327)

6.   Draw a neat, well-labelled diagram showing the four thermal zones of the Earth's atmosphere and the variation of temperature with altitude in the atmosphere. (Fig. 12.5)

CHAPTER 13: Winds, Weather, and Deserts

I.   Multiple Choice Questions

1.   The highest wind speed ever recorded on the surface of the Earth is

      a.   92 km/h
x   b.   372 km/h
      c.   118 km/hr
      d.   55 km/h

2.   Which one of the following statements is false?

x   a.   The outward spiraling flow in an anticyclone causes a zone of convergence, with divergence aloft.
      b.   The inward spiraling flow in a cyclone causes a zone of convergence, with divergence aloft.
      c.   The outward spiraling flow in an anticyclone causes a zone of divergence, with convergence aloft.
      d.   All of these statements can be true under certain circumstances.

3.   Winds that result from a balance between pressure-gradient flow and the Coriolis deflection are called

x   a.   geostrophic winds.
      b.   Hadley cells.
      c.   Ferrell cells.
      d.   convergent and divergent flow

4. Which one of the following does not affect wind speed and direction?

    a.   the Coriolis effect
x   b.   the Bergeron effect
    c.   the air pressure gradient
    d.   friction

5. Which one of the following does not belong with the others?

    a.   katabatic wind
    b.   mistral
x   c.   trade wind
    d.   bora

6. Which one of the following is not a type of local wind system?

    a.   chinook
    b.   Santa Ana
    c.   katabatic
x   d.   geostrophic

7. Which one of the following does not belong with the others?

    a.   chinook
    b.   Santa Ana
    c.   föhn
x   d.   jet stream

8. Monsoons are

    a.   characteristic of regions where local conditions bring about a seasonal reversal of the direction of surface winds.
    b.   most distinct in Asia and Africa.
    c.   responsible for hot, humid weather and torrential rains suring the summer months in Asia.
x   d.   All of the above are true.

9.   An area of relatively high air pressure, characterized by diverging winds, is called a

     a.   Hadley cell.
     b.   geostrophic wind.
     c.   tradewind.
x   d.   high.

10. A line connecting places of equal air pressure at sea level is called a(n)

     a.   equilibrium line.
     b.   front.
x   c.   isobar.
     d.   convergence zone.

11. Which one of the following is not a variable that influences wind speed or direction?

     a.   air pressure gradients
x   b.   Ekman spirals
     c.   the Coriolis effect
     d.   friction

12. A zone of low precipitation that occurs on the downwind side of mountain ranges is called a

     a.   desert.
     b.   continental desert.
     c.   chinook.
x   d.   rainshadow.

13. At high altitudes, air flow is basically a balance between pressure-gradient flow and Coriolis deflection, but at low altitudes the flow is complicated by

     a.   Ekman spiraling.
     b.   convergence and divergence.
     c.   windchill factors.
x   d.   frictional effects.

14. Which one of the following does not belong with the others?

x   a.   hurricane
      b.   tornado
      c.   funnel cloud
      d.   F-scale

15. Which one of the following does not belong with the others?

      a.   cyclone
x   b.   monsoon
      c.   typhoon
      d.   hurricane

16. Which one of the following does not belong with the others?

      a.   Hadley cells
x   b.   jet stream
      c.   intertropical convergence zone
      d.   tradewinds

17. Cloudy, unsettled weather is typically associated with the presence of a

x   a.   low-pressure center.
      b.   high-pressure center.
      c.   geostrophic wind.
      d.   tradewind.

18. Deserts of various kinds total about _____ percent of the land area of the world outside the polar regions.

      a.   10
      b.   15
x   c.   25
      d.   35

19. Hurricanes start as

x   a.   cyclones over warm ocean water.
     b.   anticyclones over coastal zones.
     c.   spiraling columns of air that extend downward from cumulonimbus clouds.
     d.   cold, dense air masses that flow under the influence of gravity.

20. A violent, upward-spiraling column of air associated with cumulonimbus clouds is called a(n)

     a.   thunderstorm.
     b.   monsoon.
x   c.   tornado.
     d.   Ekman spiral.

II.   Fill-Ins

1. Wind speeds and wind directions are controlled by _____ , _____ , and _____ .

(air pressure gradients...the Coriolis effect...friction)

2. A line connecting places of equal air pressure at sea level is called a(n) _____ .

(isobar)

3. Spiral air flow directed in towards a low-pressure area is called a(n) _____ .

(cyclone)

4. Spiral air flow outward from a high-pressure area is called a(n) _____ .

(anticyclone)

5. Cyclones rotate in a(n) _____ direction in the northern hemisphere and in a(n) _____ direction in the southern hemisphere.

(clockwise...counterclockwise)

6. In local wind systems, the flow of cold, dense air under the influence of gravity is called a(n) _____ wind .

    (katabatic)

7. A tornado funnel is called a(n) _____ if it stays aloft and a(n) _____ if it hits the ground.

    (funnel cloud...tornado)

8. The zone of low precipitation that occurs on the downwind side of mountain ranges is called a(n) _____ .

    (rainshadow)

9. Upper-atmosphere westerly winds associated with the steep pressure gradient over the polar front are called the _____ .

    (polar front jet stream)

10. The low-pressure zone of convergence located along the Equator is called the _____ .

    (intertropical convergence zone)

III. Definitions

1. air pressure gradient: the air pressure drop per unit distance.

2. anticyclone: air spiraling outward away from a high-pressure center.

3. convergence: the coming together of air masses, caused by the inward spiral flow in a cyclone and leading to an upward flow of air at the center of the low-pressure center.

4. cyclone: air spiraling inward around a low-pressure center.

5. divergence: the separation of air masses in different directions, caused by the outward spiral flow in an anticyclone and leading to an outward flow of air from the center of a high-pressure center.

6. friction: the resistance to movement when two bodies are in contact.

7. geostrophic wind: a wind that results from a balance between pressure-gradient flow and the Coriolis deflection.

8. Hadley cell: convection cells on both sides of the equator that dominate the winds in tropical and equatorial regions.

9. high (H): an area of relatively high air pressure, characterized by diverging winds.

10. intertropical convergence zone: a low-pressure zone of convergent air masses caused by warm air rising in the tropics.

11. isobar: lines on a map connecting places of equal air pressure.

12. low (L): an area of relatively low air pressure, characterized by converging winds, ascending air, and precipitation.

13. polar front: a low-pressure zone of convergence created where cold, dry air flowing towards the equator from the polar cells meets the middle-latitude belt of surface westerlies in the Ferrel cells.

14. wind: horizontal air movement arising from differences in air pressure.

15. windchill factor: the heat loss from exposed skin as a result of the combined effects of low temperature and wind speed.

IV. True-False Questions: Answers (T) or (F) are given at the end of each question.

1. Friction between air and the ground slows winds and therefore increases the Coriolis effect. (F)

2. Windchill is what happens when the air temperature drops as a result of high winds. (F)

3. If the Earth did not rotate, wind would blow in a straight line. (T)

4. Air pressures vary both horizontally and vertically in the atmosphere. (T)

5. The speed of a moving object influences the magnitude of the Coriolis effect. (T)

6. Air spiraling around a low-pressure center is called a cyclone; air spiraling around a high-pressure center is called an anticyclone. (T)

7. The outward spiraling flow in an anticyclone causes convergence, with upward movement of air and divergence aloft. (F)

8. A westerly is a wind that flows toward the west. (F)

9. The process that creates Ekman spirals is the same in the atmosphere as in the ocean. (T)

10. Isobars are lines on a map connecting places of equal air temperature. (F)

V. Short-Answer Questions

1. What are the five types of desert? Give an example of each.

Answer: (1) subtropical: Sahara, Sind, Kalahari, Great Australian; (2) continental: Gobi, Takla Makan; (3) rainshadow: deserts on the sheltered side of Sierra Nevada, Cascades, and Andes; (4) coastal: coastal Peru and southwestern Africa; (5) polar: northern Greenland, ice-free areas of Antarctica

2. Explain how windchill works.

Answer: Immediately adjacent to the human body is a thin layer of still air called a boundary layer. Heat escaping from the body must pass through the boundary layer by conduction. Because air is a poor conductor, the boundary layer serves as an effective insulator. As windspeed increases, the thickness of the boundary layer decreases, thereby reducing its effectiveness as an insulator and increasing the rate at which heat is lost from the body. For a given air temperature and given wind speed, the windchill factor is the air temperature at which exposed parts of the body would lose heat at the same rate if there were no wind.

3. What are the four variables that influence the formation of air masses?

Answer: The four variables that affect air masses are whether the mass forms: (1) over a continent (c), (2) over a maritime region (m), (3) in the tropics (T), or (4) in polar regions (P).

4.   What is a katabatic wind? Give an example of a katabatic wind.

Answer: Katabatic winds are masses of cold, dense air that flow under the influence of gravity. They occur in places where a mass of cold air accumulates over a high plateau or in a high valley in the interior of a mountain range. As the cold air accumulates, some eventually spills over a low pass or divide and flows down valleys onto the adjacent lowlands as a high-speed, cold wind. Examples include the mistral in the Rhone Valley; the bora in Yugoslavia; and Cape Dennison in Antarctica.

5.   What are the names and characteristics of the four basic types of air mass?

Answer: (1) continental polar (cP); cold temperature, low humidity; (2) maritime polar (mP); cold temperature, high humidity; (3) continental tropical (cT); hot temperature, high humidity; (4) maritime tropical (mT); warm temperature, high humidity

6.   What causes lightning and thunder? Why do they occur together?

Answer: Lightning and thunder are created by electrical charges tha form during the growth of a cumulonimbus cloud. The turbulent movement of precipitation inside the cloud causes particles in the upper part to become positively charged and particles in the lower part to become negatively charged. The charges can be released by a lightning strike either to the ground or to another cloud. As the lightning strike passes, it heats the surrounding air so rapidly that the air expands explosively and we hear the effect as thunder.

7.   What is the difference between a hurricane and a typhoon?

Answer: There is no difference; violent oceanic cyclones are called hurricanes when they occur in the Atlantic, and typhoons when they occur in the Pacific.

VI.   Longer-Answer Questions, Essays & Critical Thinking Questions: Answers are not provided for these questions (because each student will formulate his or her answer differently), but page numbers for text references are given at the end of each question.

1.   What is a Hadley cell? Describe the relationship among Hadley cells, the intertropical convergence zone, and the northeast and southeast trade winds. (p. 344-345)

2.   What is a Rossby wave? How are Rossby waves responsible for altering the jet streams? (p. 346-347)

3.   Describe four important types of local wind systems. (p. 351-352)

4.   Explain how the flow of air across a desert surface can initiate a dust storm. (p. 349-350)

5.   What is a jet stream? Explain how they form, and why they occur where they do. (p. 346)

CHAPTER 14: The Earth's Climate System

I.   Multiple Choice Questions

1.   Which one of the following is not evidence found in seafloor sediments, suggesting a succession of glacial-interglacial cycles?

    a.   The biologic component of seafloor sediments shows repeated shifts from warm interglacial biota to cold glacial biota.

    b.   The percentage of calcium carbonate in cores from some ocean regions fluctuates, indicating variations in the temperature of seawater.

    c.   The ^{18}O to ^{16}O isotope ratio fluctuates with a pattern similar to that shown in the biologic and mineral fractions of the sediments.

x   d.   Fossils of windborne pollen preserve evidence for plant successions varying in response to changing climate.

2.   The overall rise in the annual mean temperature of the world's land surfaces over the past century and a quarter has been about

    a.   0.5°C

x   b.   0.85°C

    c.   5°C

    d.   8°C

3.   Which one of these subsystems of the Earth's climate system is not driven and regulated primarily by solar energy?

    a.   cryosphere

x   b.   lithosphere

    c.   atmosphere

    d.   biosphere

4. Which one of the following statements is false?

    a. The ocean is a great reservoir of heat energy.
    b. The ocean is extremely important in controlling the composition of the atmosphere.
x   c. Seawater is essentially free of carbon dioxide, which resides mainly in the atmospheric reservoir.
    d. Changes in the ocean can bring about changes in world climate.

5. Which one of the following is not one of the ways in which topography influences climate?

    a. distribution of land masses
    b. relief of land masses
    c. shape of ocean basins
x   d. reflectivity of land surfaces

6. Which one of the following is not one of the ways in which vegetation influences climate?

x   a. extent of glaciers
    b. reflectivity of land surfaces
    c. local humidity and cloud cover
    d. wind erosion and dustiness of atmosphere

7. A climate proxy is

x   a. a natural event or phenomenon that is controlled by, and closely mimics, climate.
    b. a cyclical change in oxygen isotope ratios marking the shift from glacial to interglacial periods.
    c. an anomalous feature suggesting that climate has changed, such as channel systems remaining from now-dry streams, or the remains of dead trees above the present treeline.
    d. a period of abnormal weather lasting at least a decade.

8. Which one of the following is not used by scientists as a climate proxy?

    a. frequency of major dust-fall events in China
    b. number of weeks per year during which sea ice reached the coast of Iceland
x   c. the presence of glacial features in now-temperate lands
    d. the severity of winters in England

9.   Which one of the following is not used by scientists as a climate proxy?

      a.   the width and density of tree rings
x   b.   the presence of surface soils incompatible with present climate
      c.   oscillations in the growth rings of corals
      d.   variations in oxygen isotopes in ice cores from Greenland and Antarctica

10.   Tree rings

      a.   record the response of tree growth to variations in atmospheric dust.
x   b.   allow specialists to reconstruct past temperature and precipitation patterns over broad geographic areas.
      c.   are useful in recording climatic changes, although in general they are not as sensitive as coral growth rings.
      d.   record past climatic changes through the variation of oxygen isotopic ratios.

11.   The Little Ice Age was

      a.   an interval of cool climate that occurred about 700 years ago.
      b.   a period during which sea ice expanded in the North Atlantic.
      c.   a period during which wheat prices rose in Western Europe.
x   d.   All of the above are true.

12.   A period of cooler than average climate that occurred about 700 years ago, marked by unusually snowy winters, rainy summers, and violent storms throughout Western Europe, is referred to as the

      a.   glaciation.
      b.   Holocene Period.
      c.   Holocene Epoch.
x   d.   Little Ice Age.

13.   The last glacial maximum occurred

      a.   during the Little Ice Age.
x   b.   about 20,000 years ago.
      c.   during the 1810-1819 decade, the coldest decade in Europe since the seventeenth century.
      d.   during the Holocene Epoch.

14. The last glaciation

      a.   occurred during the Pleistocene Epoch.
      b.   culminated about 20,000 years ago.
      c.   caused central and eastern Canada and the northern part of the United States to be covered with a vast ice sheet.
x   d.   All of the above are true.

15. Which one of the following has been used as evidence to establish the date when ice sheets reached their maximum extent during the last Pleistocene glaciation?

x   a.   radiocarbon ages of buried trees
      b.   variations in oxygen isotope ratios
      c.   the presence of glacial features in now-temperate lands
      d.   surface soils with profiles that are incompatible with the present climate

16. Deep-sea sediment cores indicate that there were about _____ glacial-interglacial cycles during the Pleistocene Epoch.

      a.   four
      b.   sixteen
x   c.   thirty
      d.   sixty

17. Evidence from oxygen isotopic ratios suggests that during each Pleistocene glaciation the total volume of ice covering the land was

x   a.   about the same.
      b.   less than during the previous glaciation.
      c.   more than during the previous glaciation.
      d.   similar to that of today.

18. During the last glaciation the basin of Great Salt Lake in the western United States was occupied by a gigantic water body that geologists refer to as

      a.   Lake Baikal.
      b.   the Great Lakes.
x   c.   Lake Bonneville.
      d.   ancient Lake Michigan.

19. Which one of the following was not characteristic of conditions during the Middle Cretaceous Period?

      a.   the absence of polar ice sheets
      b.   intermediate and deep waters in the oceans 15° to 20°C warmer than now
      c.   average global temperatures 6° to 14°C warmer than today
x   d.   sea levels 100 to 200 m lower than today
      e.   All of the above are true.

20. Scientists infer that, during the height of the glacial age, the middle latitudes were both windier and dustier than they are today, because

      a.   glacial age loess deposits contain fossil plants and animals consistent with cold, dry conditions.
      b.   loess deposits in eastern Europe lie downwind from extensive glacial meltwater sediments.
      c.   the thick loess deposits of central China lie east of desert basins in central Asia that were swept by cold, dry winds during glacial times.
x   d.   All of the above are true.

II.   Fill-Ins

1. An interval during which the Earth's global ice cover greatly exceeded that of today is called a(n) _____ .

    (glaciation)

2. Periods between glacial epochs are called _____ .

    (interglaciations) or (interglacial periods)

3. Records of natural events that are controlled by, and closely mimic, climate are called _____ .

    (climate proxy records)

4. The most recent glaciation reached a maximum about _____ years ago.

    (20,000)

5. A period that occurred about 700 years ago, marked by unusually snowy winters, rainy summers, and violent storms throughout Western Europe, is referred to as the _____ .

    (Little Ice Age)

6. A measure of the circularity of a planet's orbit is its _____ .

    (eccentricity)

7. During the last glaciation the basin of Great Salt Lake in the western United States was occupied by a gigantic water body that geologists refer to as _____ .

    (Lake Bonneville)

8. Paleomagnetic dating of deep-sea sediment cores shows that the most recent glacial-interglacial cycles average about _____ years long.

    (100,000)

9. A plumelike mass of unusually hot rock rising from the base of the mantle is called a(n) _____ .

    (superplume)

10. The last glaciation occurred during the _____ Epoch.

    (Pleistocene)

III. Definitions

1. glaciation: the modification of the land surface by the action of glacier ice.

2. interglaciation: period between glacial epochs.

IV. True-False Questions

1. Over the past 100 years, the overall trend in temperatures has been upward. (T)

2. The last glaciation culminated about 10,000 years ago. (F)

3. The ocean is a great reservoir of heat energy. (T)

4. Seawater is essentially free of carbon dioxide, which resides mainly in the atmospheric reservoir. (F)

5. The ocean is extremely important in controlling the composition of the atmosphere. (T)

6. Changes in the ocean can bring about changes in world climate. (T)

7. Scientists know that a change in global climate is occurring if several years of abnormal weather occur. (F)

8. Weather trends that persist for a decade or may signal a shift to a new climatic regime. (T)

9. The overall rise in the annual mean temperature of the world's land surfaces over the past century and a quarter has been about 5°C. (F)

10. During the period between 1880 and 1940, the latitudinal limits of some plants and animals expended slightly toward the poles in response to long-term increases in average surface temperature. (T)

11. The Earth experienced four glacial ages during the Pleistocene Epoch. (F)

12. The Earth experienced a long succession of glaciations during the Pleistocene Epoch. (T)

13. Evidence of glaciation on land generally is incomplete and interrupted by many unconformities, whereas seafloor sediments provide a continuous historical record of climatic change. (T)

14. Variations of oxygen isotopes in deep-sea sediment cores reveal that the ocean has grown colder over the last 50 million years. (T)

V. Short-Answer Questions

1. How can large volcanic eruptions contribute to changes in climate?

Answer: Large explosive volcanic eruptions can eject huge quantities of fine ash into the atmosphere to create a veil of fine dust that encircles the globe. Like other types of dust, the fine ash particles tend to scatter incoming solar radiation, resulting in a slight cooling at the Earth's surface. Although the dust settles out rather quickly, generally within a few months to a year, tiny droplets of sulfuric acid, produced by the interaction of volcanically emitted SO_2 gas and water vapor, also scatter the Sun's rays, and such droplets remain in the upper atmosphere for several years.

2.   How can ice cores tell us that climates were both windy and dusty during glacial times?

Answer: Studies of ice cores from the Greenland Ice Sheet indicate that the percentage of wind-blown dust rises significantly in the part of the cores that corresponds to the last glaciation. Because Greenland and much of northern North America were ice-covered at that time, much of the dust likely originated along the valleys of braided meltwater streams that crossed windy periglacial zones bordering the ice sheets in North America and Eurasia.

3.   What are some of the most reliable climate proxy records available?

Answer: (Any of the following): frequency of major dust-fall events in China; severity of winters in England in terms of number of mild or severe months; number of weeks per year during which sea ice reached the coast of Iceland; freezing date of Lake Suwa in Japan; the number of severe winters in China since the sixth century A.D.; the height of the Nile River at Cairo since A.D. 622; the quality of wine harvests in Germany since the ninth century A.D.; dates for the blooming of cherry trees in Kyoto, Japan, since A.D. 812; wheat prices (a reflection of climatic adversity); variations of oxygen isotope ratios in ice cores from Greenland and Antarctica; variations in the width and density of tree rings; and variations in the growth rings of corals.

4.   How do fossil pollen grains from lake-bottom sediments indicate past climates?

Answer: At any given level in a sediment core, pollen grains reveal the assemblage of plants that flourished near the site when the sediments were deposited. If scientists can find a modern vegetation assemblage that has a composition like that implied by the fossil pollen, then the precipitation and temperature at the site of the modern assemblage can be used to estimate climatic conditions represented by the fossil assemblage.

5.   Why does Europe now have only 30 naturally occurring species of trees, while North America has 130 species?

Answer: In North America, migrating plants driven south by ice during the last glaciation could inhabit the relatively warmer lowlands that extended to the Gulf of Mexico. But in Europe, the glacier-clad Alps constituted a high, cold barrier north of the Mediterranean Sea. Many species were trapped between the large ice sheet to the north and the Alpine glaciers to the south and were driven to extinction.

VI. **Longer-Answer Questions, Essays & Critical Thinking Questions:** Answers are not provided for these questions (because each student will formulate his or her answer differently), but page numbers of text references are given at the end of each question.

1.   Explain how variations in oxygen isotope ratios can be used as a climate proxy record. (p. 366, 375)

2.   Name at least five commonly used climate proxy records. In what ways are each of these natural events or phenomena related to or controlled by climate? (p. 365-367, 385-386)

3.   How can loess deposits be used to infer that, during the height of the glacial age, the middle latitudes were both windier and dustier than today? (p. 369-370)

4.   Why are fossil pollen grains particularly useful to scientists in reconstructing past climatic conditions? (p. 371-372)

5.   Summarize the major types of evidence for changes in temperature and precipitation during glacial ages. (p. 373-374).

6.   Discuss the possible connections between the unusually high rate of volcanic activity and the exceptionally warm climate during the Middle Cretaceous Period. (p. 378-381)

7.   Explain how variations in the eccentricity, tilt, and precession of the Earth's orbit may influence climate. (p. 381-382)

8.   Studies show that methane and carbon dioxide concentrations in the atmosphere were low, and the proportion of fine atmospheric dust was high during glacial ages as compared to interglaciations. Explain how these factors may have worked together to amplify temperature changes during glacial times. (p. 382-383)

9.   Explain how changes in the ocean's thermohaline circulation may affect climate. (p. 383-384)

CHAPTER 15: Dynamics of the Global Ecosystem

I.   Multiple Choice Questions

1.   What makes the Earth unique among planets is the presence of

      a.   an atmosphere.
x   b.   a biosphere.
      c.   a lithosphere.
      d.   a hydrosphere.
      e.   All of the above make this planet unique.

2.   Eutrophication

      a.   generates an anoxic environment.
      b.   asphyxiates aerobic organisms living in the environment.
      c.   occurs in bodies of water with high levels of plant nutrients.
x   d.   All of the above are true.
      e.   None of the above is true.

3.   Acid mine drainage occurs whenever

      a.   underground mining is carried out.
      b.   acids formed by the combination of minerals with water are carried into the atmosphere and deposited in the form of acid precipitation.
x   c.   compounds such as pyrite are oxidized to acids (such as sulfuric acid) and enter the surrounding environment.
      d.   All of the above are true.

4.   Which one of the following is not an example of an extrinsic factor that might affect the population of an ecosystem?

x   a.   competition among species for a particular niche
      b.   a forest fire
      c.   a very severe winter
      d.   These are all examples of extrinsic factors that can affect ecosystem populations.

5.   Acid rain

     a.   is quickly neutralized when it interacts with granitic rocks.
x   b.   is quickly neutralized when it interacts with carbonate rocks.
     c.   releases toxic minerals into the atmosphere.
     d.   All of the above are true.

6.   The substance responsible for the poisoning of residents at Minamata Bay, Japan was

x   a.   mercury
     b.   arsenic
     c.   aluminum
     d.   sulfuric acid

7.   A population cycle is

     a.   the time it takes for one set of parents in a given species to reproduce itself.
x   b.   a periodic rise and fall in the population growth curve due to cyclicity in an extrinsic
          factor that affects population.
     c.   exponential growth.
     d.   the sum of the conditions that allow an organisms and its offspring to sustain
          themselves and breed.

8.   Which one of the following is not an example of an intrinsic factor that might affect the
     population of an ecosystem?

     a.   competition among species for a limited food supply
x   b.   climatic change
     c.   predation
     d.   disease
     e.   These are all examples of intrinsic factors that can affect ecosystem populations.

9.   The greatest mass extinction in Earth history, in which 95% of known fossil species became
     extinct, occurred at the

     a.   Cretaceous-Tertiary boundary.
x   b.   Permian-Triassic boundary.
     c.   Paleozoic-Proterozoic boundary.
     d.   Pleistocene-Holocene boundary.

10. Heterotrophs

x   a.   are unable to use the energy from sunlight directly.
     b.   are carnivores.
     c.   are primary producers.
     d.   All of the above are true.

11. The term homeostasis refers to a condition of _____ in an ecosystem.

x   a.   balance
     b.   positive feedback
     c.   low diversity
     d.   All of the above are true.

12. The principle of competitive exclusion says that

x   a.   in a given ecosystem, one species generally occupies one niche to the exclusion of other species.
     b.   diversity in an ecosystem is defined by the number of species in the ecosystem.
     c.   the larger the niches in an ecosystem, the lower the diversity; the smaller the niches, the greater the diversity.
     d.   intrinsic factors such as competition for food can limit population growth in a given species.

13. Which one of the following does not belong with the others?

     a.   climax community
     b.   homeostasis
x   c.   heterotroph
     d.   negative feedback

14. Provinciality

     a.   is high at the present time.
     b.   correlates positively with biological diversity.
     c.   is enhanced by the presence of climatic or geographic barriers.
x   d.   All of the above are true.

15. A marked increase in global biological diversity occurred

    a.   in Late Proterozoic time.
    b.   after the advent of nucleated cells.
    c.   after sufficient oxygen had accumulated in the atmosphere to allow respiration.
x   d.   All of the above are true.

16. Mammals originated in the _____ Period.

    a.   Holocene
    b.   Cretaceous
x   c.   Triassic
    d.   Proterozoic

17. Early mammals

x   a.   were very small.
    b.   rapidly began to dominate the available food supply.
    c.   had relatively slow metabolisms.
    d.   All of the above are true.

18. In the marine environment, the ecosystems with the highest diversity are found in

    a.   the abyssal plain.
    b.   the vicinity of black smokers.
    c.   Kuroshio current.
x   d.   the continental shelves of the intertropical region.

19. Acid rain

    a.   forms when coal is burned, releasing sulfur.
    b.   can acidify aquatic ecosystems.
    c.   has been reported to cause damage to crops.
x   d.   All of the above are true.

20. Scientists use AVHRR images taken from satellites to study

    a.   deforestation.
    b.   desertification.
    c.   changes in the biosphere.
x   d.   All of the above are true.

II.   Fill-Ins

1. _____ , which get their energy from inorganic sources, form the bottom of the food chain.

   (Autotrophs)

2. Heterotrophs feed on autotrophs or other heterotrophs, thereby creating a(n) _____ in which energy is moved upward from level to level via the food chain.

   (trophic pyramid)

3. A(n) _____ is a trophic pyramid plus the habitat in which the pyramid exists.

   (ecosystem)

4. The global ecosphere, also known as the _____ , is the sum of all the smaller ecosystems on the Earth.

   (biosphere)

5. Ecological balance is commonly maintained by _____ feedback.

   (negative)

6. The resources of an ecosystem limit the population; the limit is known as the _____ .

   (carrying capacity)

7. The richest and most diverse part of the biosphere on land is the _____ .

   (equatorial rain forest)

8. The biosphere is a consumer hierarchy in which autotrophs are at the base, _____ (plant-eating heterotrophs) are on the next level up, and they in turn are devoured by _____ (meat-eating heterotrophs) and _____ (heterotrophs that eat both meat and plants) at the top.

    (herbivores...carnivores..omnivores)

9. The pathways by which energy (as food) is moved from one trophic level to another are called _____ .

    (food chains)

10. Globally, the present rate of soil erosion is about _____ tons per year.

    (25 billion)

III. Definitions

1. anaerobic: without oxygen.

2. autotrophs: organisms that can get energy directly from sunlight.

3. carnivores: meat-eating heterotrophs.

4. carrying capacity: the limit on the population that an ecosystem can carry, imposed by the limited resources of that ecosystem.

5. chemoautotrophs: organisms that derive energy from the oxidation of hydrogen sulfide in the water discharged from black smokers.

6. ecological niche: the sum of the conditions (including habitat and resources) that allow an organism and its offspring to sustain themselves and breed.

7. ecosystem: a trophic pyramid and its habitat.

8. eutrophication: bodies of water with a high level of plant nutrients and consequently high levels of algae growth.

9. food chains: the pathways by which energy (as food) is moved from one trophic level to another.

10. food web: the map of all interconnections among food chains for an ecosystem.

11. herbivores: plant-eating heterotrophs.

12. heterotrophs: organisms that are unable to use the energy from sunlight directly and so must get their energy by eating autotrophs or other heterotrophs.

13. homeostasis: the maintenance of fairly constant internal conditions; a balance within an ecosystem.

14. negative feedback: the influence of a product on the process that produces it, such that production decreases with the growth of the product.

15. omnivores: heterotrophs that eat both meat and plants.

16. positive feedback: the influence of a product on the process that produces it, such that production increases the growth of the product.

17. provinciality: the extent to which the global ecosystem is divided into subsystems by barriers to the migration of organisms.

18. species: a population of individuals that can interbreed to produce offspring that are, in turn, interfertile with each other.

19. symbiotic: a close, long-term relationship between individuals of different species.

20. trophic pyramid: the hierarchy of organisms in which energy is moved from one level to the next.

IV. True-False Questions

1. Most autotrophs are green plants. (T)

2. The transfer of energy through a trophic pyramid involves a lot of wasted energy. (T)

3. Unchecked population growth is an example of negative feedback. (F)

4. Globally, the present rate of soil erosion is about 5 billion tons per year. (F)

5. Without the lithosphere there would be no soil. (T)

6. There is conclusive evidence that a gigantic meteorite impact at the end of the Cretaceous Period caused the extinction of the dinosaurs. (F)

7. Species with a wide range of tolerance for environmental conditions are called generalists. (T)

8. Species which occupy narrowly defined niches are called provincial. (F)

9. As a population approaches the carrying capacity of its ecosystem, it will begin to die out and eventually become extinct. (F)

10. In exponential growth, the rate of increase at any instant is equal to the size of the population times a constant. (T)

V.   Short-Answer Questions

1. What are the five most important factors that influence biological diversity?

Answer: (1) climate; (2) sexual reproduction; (3) evolutionary innovations; (4) provinciality; and (5) niche availability

2. What is it called when an ecosystem is divided into subsystems by barriers? Explain how geographic barriers can influence diversity.

Answer: The extent to which an ecosystem is divided into subsystems by barriers is called provinciality. Geographic barriers such as seaways or mountains between landmasses, or land between seas, can prevent the migration of species and keep them apart. The more the system is separated, the greater will be the diversity because a given niche in each subsystem can be occupied by a different species without competition.

3. What is the principle of competitive exclusion?

Answer: In a given ecosystem, one species generally occupies one niche to the exclusion of other species.

4. How does the number and size of niches in an ecosystem influence its diversity?

Answer: Because diversity in an ecosystem is the number of species in it and because each species occupies a particular niche, the diversity of an ecosystem is the number of occupied niches in it. The larger the niches in an ecosystem, the fewer the species in that ecosystem (in other words, a low diversity system) because each niche takes up more of the total resource space; the smaller the niches, the more species in the ecosystem (high diversity).

5. The most important element contributed by the lithosphere to the biosphere is phosphorus. Why?

Answer: Phosphorus plays two essential roles: in the form of sugar-phosphate units, phosphorus forms the helical framework of the DNA molecule, and as adenosine mono-diphosphate and adenosine triphosphate it serves as the currency for all of life's energy transactions.

VI. Longer-Answer Questions, Essays & Critical Thinking Questions: Answers are not provided for these questions (because each student will formulate his or her answer differently), but page numbers for text references are given at the end of each question.

1. In what ways has the process of plate tectonics influenced biological diversity in the global ecosphere? (p. 403-405)

2. Describe the major linkages between the biosphere and the atmosphere. (p. 405)

3. Describe the contributions of the mantle to life on Earth. (p. 406-407)

4. What is a black smoker? Why was the discovery of black smokers significant in terms of our understanding of life-supporting processes on Earth? (p. 406-407)

5. How can evolutionary innovations enable a group of organisms to diversify? Give at least one example to support your answer. (p. 402)

6. What is the difference between extrinsic and intrinsic factors that can limit population growth in an ecosystem? Give and example of each type of factor, taken either from the book or from your own experience. (p. 395)

CHAPTER 16: Evolution of the Biosphere

I.   Multiple Choice Questions

1.   The stringing together of small molecules to make large chain- or sheet-like molecules is called

      a.   crystallization.
      b.   metabolism.
x   c.   polymerization.
      d.   chemosynthesis.

2.   The packing of atoms or molecules in ordered geometric arrays is called

      a.   polymerization.
x   b.   crystallization.
      c.   chemosynthesis.
      d.   proteinization.

3.   Stromatolites are

x   a.   layered structures made of calcium carbonate precipitated by blue-green algae.
      b.   among the earliest fossil procaryotic cells.
      c.   found only in very ancient rocks.
      d.   All of the above are true.

4.   Metabolism is

      a.   a form of biopolymerization.
x   b.   the sum of all chemical reactions by which organisms grow and maintain themselves.
      c.   the stringing together of small molecules to make large chain- or sheet-like molecules.
      d.   the sum of the changes that organisms and populations of organisms undergo through time.

5. The changes that organisms and population undergo through time are called

    x   a.   evolution.
        b.   biosynthesis.
        c.   metabolism.
        d.   biogeochemical cycles.

6. Deoxyribonucleic acid is

        a.   DNA.
        b.   a biopolymer.
        c.   held together by bases.
    x   d.   All of the above are true.

7. Aerobic eucaryotes

    x   a.   use oxygen for respiration.
        b.   cannot form three-dimensional structures.
        c.   require a large surface-to-volume ratio in order to allow for rapid diffusion of food in and waste out.
        d.   All of the above are true.

8. The earliest fossils of multicellular organisms are found in rocks about _____ years old.

        a.   60 million
    x   b.   600 million
        c.   1.4 billion
        d.   3.5 billion

9. Enzymes

        a.   are proteins.
        b.   catalyze chemical reactions in organisms.
        c.   facilitate the polymerization of amino acids to form proteins.
    x   d.   All of the above are true.

10. Before about _____ years ago the Earth's atmosphere was deficient in oxygen.

  x   a.   1.5 billion
        b.   15 billion
        c.   15 million
        d.   1.5 million

11. Which one of the following is not a form in which nitrogen occurs in nature?

        a. N_2
        b. NO_3
  x   c. NO_2H
        d. NH_3

12. The most ancient fossil procaryotes are found in rocks about _____ years old.

        a.   1.5 billion
        b.   2 billion
  x   c.   3.5 billion
        d.   3.9 billion

13. Which one of the following does not belong with the others?

        a.   Phanerozoic
        b.   Proterozoic
  x   c.   Cenozoic
        d.   Archean

14. What unusual feature was shared by almost all of the Ediacaran animals?

        a.   very large
  x   b.   flat
        c.   disc-shaped
        d.   branching structures

15.　The Cambrian Period

x　a.　was a time of incredible biological diversity in Earth history.
　　b.　marked the end of the Phanerozoic Eon.
　　c.　was the period during which the first winged insects developed.
　　d.　All of the above are true.

16.　The earliest land plants were

　　a.　angiosperms.
x　b.　seedless.
　　c.　gymnosperms.
　　d.　enclosed-seed plants.

17.　A chordate is

　　a.　a type of jawless fish, prevalent in the Devonian Period.
x　b.　an animal that possesses a notochord.
　　c.　a type of amphibian, one of the first creatures to venture out on land.
　　d.　a precursor of the mammal.

18.　The first animals to make the change from sea to land were

x　a.　arthropods.
　　b.　crossopterygians.
　　c.　chordates.
　　d.　stromatolites.

19.　Land plants provide themselves with an internal aquatic environment through

　　a.　pollination.
　　b.　spores.
x　c.　vascular systems.
　　d.　diffusion.

20. Which one of the following does not belong with the others?

      a.   panspermia
      b.   outer space
      c.   carbonaceous chondrites
x   d.   symbiosis

II.   Fill-Ins

1. The first skeletons evolved in the _____ Period.

    (Cambrian)

2. Details of cell production are passed on from cell to cell, generation after generation, through information stored in _____ .

    (DNA) or (deoxyribonucleic acid)

3. _____ is the synthesis of small organic molecules such as amino acids from gases in the atmosphere or in space.

    (Chemosynthesis)

4. _____ is the polymerization of small organic molecules to form biopolymers such as proteins.

    (Biosynthesis)

5. Anaerobic procaryotes get their energy through the process of _____ , whereas eucaryotes obtain their energy through the process of _____ .

    (fermentation...respiration)

6. Layered structures composed of calcium carbonate precipitated by blue-green algae are called _____ .

    (stromatolites)

7. The earliest known multicellular organisms are found in rocks _____ years old.

    (3.5 billion)

8. In the Permian-Triassic extinction, about _____ percent of all species alive at the time were lost, and about _____ percent of all species were lost in the Cretaceous-Tertiary extinction.

    (95...77)

9. The set of chemical reactions through which an organism grows and maintains itself is called _____ .

    (metabolism)

10. The hypothesis that life originated in outer space and was then dispersed to other parts of the universe, including the Earth, is called _____ .

    (panspermia)

III. Definitions

1. amino acid: organic molecule containing an amino (NH_2) group; the building block of proteins.

2. angiosperm: a plant whose seeds are surrounded by fruit.

3. biogeochemical cycles: a natural cycle describing the movements and interactions through the Earth's spheres of the chemicals essential to life.

4. biosynthesis: the polymerization of small organic molecules within a living organism to form biopolymers, particularly proteins.

5. cell: the basic structural unit of all living organisms.

6. chemosynthesis: the synthesis of small organic molecules such as amino acids.

7. cytoplasm: the main body of the cell, excluding the nucleus and the plasma membrane.

8. deoxyribonucleic acid (DNA): a biopolymer consisting of two twisted, chainlike molecules held together by organic molecules called bases; the genetic material for all organisms except viruses, it stores the information on how to make proteins.

9. Ediacaran animals: the earliest fossils of multicellular organisms discovered in 600-million-year-old rocks in the Ediacara Hills of South Australia.

10. enzyme: a protein that catalyzes a chemical reaction in an organism.

11. eucaryotic cell (eucaryotes): a cell that includes a nucleus with a membrane, as well as other membrane-bound organelles.

12. evolution: the changes that species undergo through time, eventually leading to the formation of new species.

13. gymnosperms: naked-seed plants.

14. metabolism: the sum of all the chemical reactions in an organisms, by which it grows and maintains itself.

15. organelles: a well-defined cell part that has a particular function in the operation of the cell.

16. paleontologist: a scientist who studies extinct organisms.

17. panspermia: the hypothesis of the supposed origin of life in space, followed by a diaspora to various parts of the galaxy (including the Earth).

18. procaryotic cell (procaryotes): cells without a nucleus; refers to single-celled organisms that have no membrane separating their DNA from the cytoplasm.

19. protein: molecule formed through the polymerization of an amino acid.

20. ribonucleic acid (RNA): a single-stranded molecule similar to the DNA molecule, but with a slightly different chemical composition; it reads and executes the codes contained in the DNA.

IV. True-False Questions

1. Fossil procaryotes have been found in rocks 3.5 billion years old. (T)

2. Bacteria, which are the simplest living organisms, and viruses, which are "almost" alive, were the first life forms on Earth. (F)

3. The first cell must have been an anaerobic procaryote. (T)

4. The hypothesis of panspermia states that life began in the oceans and then spread to other parts of the Earth system. (F)

5. The accumulation of oxygen in the atmosphere began at least 3.5 billion years ago. (F)

6. Procaryotes were the first type of organisms to be able to reproduce sexually. (F)

7. The Ediacaran animals are fossils of the earliest known multicellular organisms. (T)

8. The first skeletons, both internal and external, evolved in the Cambrian Period. (T)

9. The first plants were seedless. (T)

10. The first land animals, amphibians, left the sea in the early Devonian Period. (T)

11. Human beings are eucaryotes. (T)

12. Respiration is a more efficient means of obtaining energy than is fermentation. (T)

V. Short-Answer Questions

1. What are the most often-cited causes for the great mass extinctions of species that have occurred at various times in Earth history?

Answer: Possible causes of mass extinctions include giant meteorite impacts; plate tectonic rearrangements of continents; declines of sea level; prolonged volcanic eruptions; and severe climatic changes.

2. What are the three essential steps to form life?

Answer: (1) chemosynthesis; (2) biosynthesis; (3) the development of the complex cellular machinery needed for reproduction

3.   What are the four most important biogeochemical elements?

Answer: (1) carbon; (2) oxygen; (3) nitrogen; (4) phosphorus

4.   What are the four requirements that had to be met in order for life to be able to leave the sea and live on land?

Answer: (1) structural support; (2) an internal aquatic environment; (3) means for exchanging gases with air instead of with water; (4) a moist environment for the reproductive system.

5.   What is the most widely held hypothesis for the cause of the Cretaceous-Tertiary extinction?

Answer: The most widely held hypothesis is that the impact of a large meteorite and consequent disruption of climate caused a mass extinction of species.

6.   What is the most widely held hypothesis for the cause of the Permian-Triassic extinction?

Answer: The rearrangement of landmasses into the supercontinent Pangaea, and the consequent loss of habitats is the most likely cause of this mass extinction.

7.   Describe the two ways in which atoms can be ordered into small molecules, and small molecules into larger molecules.

Answer: Ordering can occur by (1) polymerization, which is the stringing together of small molecules to make large chain- or sheet-like molecules; or (2) crystallization, which is the packing of atoms or molecules in ordered geometric arrays.

8.   What are the three essential functions of proteins?

Answer: (1) They form tissue such as muscle, ligaments, hair, and blood cells; (2) they provide patterns for laying down mineral structures such as shells and bones; and (3) as enzymes, they catalyze all chemical reactions in the organism.

VI.   Longer-Answer Questions, Essays & Critical Thinking Questions: Answers are not provided for these questions (because each student will formulate his or her answer differently), but page numbers for text references are given at the end of each question.

1.   Why is it improbable that the earliest form of life on Earth was a bacterium? (p. 417)

2. Discuss the Ediacaran fauna and their significance in terms of our understanding of early life forms on Earth. (p. 427-428)

3. What are the main hypotheses offered as explanations for the explosion of biological diversity that occurred in the Cambrian Period? (p. 428)

4. What is chemosynthesis? Discuss the early work of Oparin and Miller on chemosynthesis and the origins of life on Earth. (p. 419)

5. What lines of evidence suggest that life might have originated in space rather than on Earth? What is panspermia, and what are the pros and cons of this hypothesis for the origin of life? (p. 419-421)

6. Why is it generally agreed that the earliest forms of life on Earth must have been anaerobic? (p. 421)

7. What are some of the possible reasons for the evolution of skeletons (both internal and external) in the Cambrian Period (as opposed to an earlier development)? (p. 428-429)

CHAPTER 17: Resources from the Earth

I. Multiple Choice Questions

1. Metals were first used more than _____ years ago.

    a.   2 million
    b.   50,000
x   c.   17,000
    d.   2,000

2. Today approximately _____ kinds of minerals and fuels are mined and used.

    a.   100
x   b.   200
    c.   2000
    d.   3000

3.   Which one of the following is not a common gangue mineral?

    a.   quartz
    b.   feldspar
    c.   calcite
x d.   galena

4.   The total energy consumption of all the world's people is about

    a.   3 J per year
    b.   30 J per year
    c. 3×10^2 J per year
x d. 3×10^{20} J per year

5.   The enrichment factor necessary before a particular mineral deposit can be classified as an ore and mined economically

    a.   is approximately 2,500.
    b.   is approximately 10,000.
x c.   can vary as costs, mining and processing technologies, and demands change.
    d.   depends mainly on the geologic setting in which the mineral forms or accumulates.

6.   Which one of the following is not a nonmetallic mineral resource?

    a.   gypsum
x b.   gangue
    c.   clay
    d.   salt

7.   Which one of the following statements is false?

    a.   Before a mineral deposit can be worked profitably, the percentage of valuable metal in the deposit must be greatly enriched above its average percentage in the Earth's crust.
x b.   The enrichment factor needed for profitable mining is greatest for minerals that are present in greatest abundant in the crust.
    c.   As mining and mineral processing have become more efficient and less expensive, it has been possible to work leaner ore, so there has been a historic decline in enrichment factors.
    d.   The decline in enrichment factors has levelled off over the past twenty years, and for some metals enrichment factors have begun to increase slightly.

8. Which one of the following is not a metallic mineral resource?

  x   a.   gypsum
       b.   galena
       c.   chalcopyrite
       d.   sphalerite

9. Ores are

       a.   mineral deposits.
       b.   local enrichments of valuable minerals.
       c.   aggregates of minerals from which one or more minerals is economically extractable.
  x   d.   All of the above are true.

10. Which one of the following does not belong with the others?

       a.   hydrothermal solution
       b.   seafloor spreading center
       c.   volcanogenic massive sulfide
  x   d.   residual mineral deposit

11. ^{235}U

       a.   is the most abundant of the three naturally occurring radioactive isotopes that are mined for nuclear energy.
  x   b.   is the only natural radioactive isotope that will maintain a chain reaction during fission.
       c.   comprises about 38.8% of the total uranium atoms occurring in nature.
       d.   All of the above are true.

12. If all the possible hydropower in the world were developed, we could only satisfy about _____ of the world's energy needs.

  x   a.   one third
       b.   one half
       c.   10 percent
       d.   2 percent

13. Which one of the following is not a possible source of heat for the formation of hydrothermal solutions?

     a.   a cooling granitic stock or batholith
     b.   a magma chamber beneath a volcano
     c.   seafloor spreading center volcanism
x   d.   thermohaline circulation of seawater

14. Pegmatite is

     a.   a type of residual mineral deposit.
x   b.   a very coarse-grained igneous rock.
     c.   important as a source for gold and other metallic mineral resources.
     d.   All of the above are true.

15. Gangue is

x   a.   a nonvaluable mineral in an ore deposit.
     b.   a nonmetallic mineral resource.
     c.   a metallic mineral resource.
     d.   a type of evaporite deposit.

16. Oil that is so viscous and thick that it will not flow is called

     a.   kerogen.
x   b.   tar.
     c.   peat.
     d.   petroleum.

17. Kerogen

     a.   is present in all shales.
     b.   forms liquid and gaseous hydrocarbons when it is heated.
     c.   is a potential source of petroleum.
x   d.   All of the above are true.

18. The world's largest deposit of rich oil shale is in

x   a.   the United States.
      b.   Alberta, Canada.
      c.   Russia.
      d.   China.

19. The world's largest known occurrence of tar sand is in

      a.   the United States.
x   b.   Alberta, Canada.
      c.   Russia.
      d.   Venezuela.

20. Biomass energy includes

      a.   wood.
      b.   animal dung.
      c.   fuels derived from plant life.
x   d.   All of the above are true.

II.   Fill-Ins

1. Metals were first used more than _____ years ago.

   (17,000)

2. The concept that a hostile planet could be changed into a habitable planet like the Earth is called _____ .

   (terraforming)

3. When a mineral deposit can be worked profitably, it is called a(n) _____ .

   (ore)

4. A resource that is replenished by seasonal growth is called _____ .

   (renewable)

5. The first people to use oil as a fuel were _____ .

    (the Babylonians)

6. _____ mineral deposits form when heavy minerals are concentrated by flowing surface water in streams or along the shore.

    (Placer)

7. _____ mineral deposits form when minerals are concentrated by weathering processes.

    (Residual)

8. _____ mineral deposits form when minerals are concentrated by hot, aqueous solutions flowing through fractures and pore spaces in crustal rock.

    (Hydrothermal)

9. The level of concentration of a mineral deposit is called its _____ .

    (grade)

10. The type of sedimentary mineral deposit that forms when layers of salts precipitate out of evaporating lake water or seawater is called a(n) _____ deposit.

    (evaporite)

11. Mineral deposits in which the sulfide ore minerals occur in layers enclosed by and parallel to the sedimentary strata in which they occur are called _____ mineral deposits.

    (stratabound)

12. Large hydrothermal copper deposits associated with intrusive igneous rocks that are porphyritic in texture are called _____ deposits.

    (porphyry copper)

13. Metallogenic provinces form in response to either _____ controls or _____ controls.

    (climatic...plate tectonic)

14. When organic matter accumulates in swamps it first turns into _____ ; then, after burial, diagenesis, and (in some cases) metamorphism, it becomes _____ .

    (peat...coal)

15. Petroleum is defined as gaseous, liquid, and semi-solid naturally occurring substances that consist chiefly of _____ .

    (hydrocarbons) or (compounds of hydrogen and carbon)

III. Definitions

1. breeder reactor: a nuclear reactor in which fission takes place, specifically, the pile in which the conversion of ^{238}U takes place.

2. coal: a black, combustible, sedimentary or metamorphic rock consisting chiefly of decomposed plant matter and containing more than 50 percent organic matter.

3. fission: controlled radioactive transformation.

4. fossil fuel: remains of plants and animals trapped in sediment that may be used for fuel.

5. gangue: the nonvaluable minerals of an ore.

6. hydrothermal mineral deposit: any local concentration of minerals formed by deposition from a hydrothermal solution.

7. magmatic mineral deposit: any local concentration of minerals formed by magmatic processes in an igneous rock.

8. metallogenic provinces: limited regions of the crust within which mineral deposits occur in unusually large numbers.

9. mineral deposit: any volume of rock containing an enrichment of one or more minerals.

10. ore: an aggregate of minerals from which one or more minerals can be extracted profitably.

11. petroleum: gaseous, liquid, and semi-solid substances occurring naturally and consisting chiefly of chemical compounds of carbon and hydrogen.

12. pile: a device in which nuclear fission can be controlled.

13. placer: a deposit of heavy minerals concentrated mechanically.

14. residual mineral deposit: any local concentration of minerals formed as a result of weathering.

15. sedimentary mineral deposit: any local concentration of minerals formed through processes of sedimentation.

16. tar (asphalt): an oil that is viscous and so thick it will not flow.

IV. True-False Questions

1. No nation is entirely self-sufficient in mineral supplies. (T)

2. All ores are mineral deposits, but the reverse is not true. (T)

3. It is probable that more mineral deposits have been formed by deposition from hydrothermal solutions than by any other mechanism. (T)

4. More than half of all gold recovered throughout all of human history has come from magmatic ore deposits. (F)

5. Oil is the most abundant of the fossil fuels. (F)

6. Peat can only form in swampy, tropical conditions. (F)

7. Wood and animal dung used for cooking and heating in many parts of the world now accounts for about 34 percent of the world's total energy use. (F)

8. Approximately 8 percent of the world's electrical power is derived from nuclear power plants. (T)

9. Most of the world's geothermal steam reservoirs are close to plate boundaries. (T)

10. Wind and wave energy are both secondary expressions of solar energy. (T)

V. Short-Answer Questions

1. What are the five main types of processes through which minerals can become concentrated, and what are the resulting types of mineral deposits?

Answer: (1) precipitation from hydrothermal solutions to form hydrothermal mineral deposits; (2) concentration through crystallization to form magmatic mineral deposits; (3) concentration through evaporation or precipitation from lake water or seawater to form sedimentary mineral deposits; (4) concentration in flowing water to form placers; and (5) concentration through weathering to form residual deposits.

2. What are the two main groups of mineral resources, and in what ways are they used?

Answer: (1) metallic minerals are those from which metals such as copper, iron, gold, and zinc can be recovered by smelting; (2) nonmetallic minerals are those used for their physical or chemical properties rather than for the chemical elements they contain; examples are salt, gypsum, sodium carbonate, calcium fluoride, and clay for bricks.

3. Two mineral deposits might have the same grade and be the same size, but one is ore and the other is not. Furthermore, a particular aggregate of minerals may be an ore at one time but not at another. How might you explain this?

Answer: There could be many reasons for these differences. The uneconomic deposit could be too deeply buried or located in so remote an area that the costs of mining and transport would be so high that the final product would not be competitive with the same product from other deposits. As costs and markets prices fluctuate, an aggregate that was an ore at one time might no longer be profitable.

4. What is the origin of the rich metallogenic province that runs along the western side of the Americas, which contains the world's greatest concentration of hydrothermal copper deposits?

Answer: The deposits were formed by hydrothermal solutions generated by stratovolcanoes; the volcanoes formed above the subduction edges of the South American and North American plates. (See Fig. 17.12 in text)

5. What are some of the ways in which hydrothermal solutions can form?

Answer: Some solutions originate when water dissolved in a magma is released as the magma rises and cools; an example would be a cooling granitic stock or batholith. Other solutions are formed from rainwater or seawater that circulates deep in the crust. The magma chamber beneath a volcano can also be a source of hydrothermal solutions. Today pools of hot, dense brine are depositing ore minerals in sediments at the bottom of the Red Sea. Hot, mineral-laden springs are also associated with ocean-floor spreading centers, such as that found today at the East Pacific Rise.

6. Why is there a close connection between geothermal steam reservoirs and plate boundaries?

Answer: In most cases, the source of heat for geothermal steam is a body of magma. Most of the world's geothermal steam reservoirs are close to plate margins because plate margins are where most recent volcanic activity has occurred.

VI. Longer-Answer Questions, Essays & Critical Thinking Questions: Answers are not provided for these questions (because each student will formulate his or her answer differently), but page numbers for text references are given at the end of each question.

1. How might the process of terraforming be carried out on the planet Mars? Why is Mars the most likely candidate for terraforming? (p. 442-443)

2. Draw a series of at least three neat, well-labelled diagrams illustrating how the action of surface water in streams or along the shore can lead to the concentration of heavy minerals in placer-type deposits. (p. 454-455, Fig. 17.9)

3. What are some of the problems associated with the large scale development of wind and wave energy? (p. 465)

4. Describe the processes leading to the formation of petroleum. (p. 459-460)

5. How do residual mineral deposits form? Give two examples of important types of residual mineral deposits. (p. 455-456)

CHAPTER 18: Global Change: A Planet Under Stress

I.   Multiple Choice Questions

1.   The human population of this planet is now approaching

      a.   4 billion
      b.   5 billion
x   c.   6 billion
      d.   10 billion

2.   The atmospheric gas responsible for 80% of the natural greenhouse effect is

      a. CO_2.
x   b. H_2O.
      c.   CFCs.
      d. O_3.

3.   Even if all production of CFCs were to stop tomorrow, a recovery to natural conditions in the ozone layer would likely take

      a.   a year or more.
      b.   a decade or more.
x   c.   a century or more.
      d.   several thousand years.

4.   Which one of the following is not one of the changes that scientists predict will be associated with global climatic warming?

      a.   increased evaporation from the oceans
      b.   increased precipitation in equatorial regions
      c.   drier conditions in the central regions of large continents
x   d.   All of the above are changes that scientists predict will be associated with global climatic warming.

5. An estimated _____ percent of the Amazonian rain forest has already been cleared.

      a.   2
x   b.   12
      c.   20
      d.   41

6. Which one of the following is not a form in which oxygen occurs naturally in the atmosphere?

      a. O
      b. O_2
      c. O_3
x   d. O_4

7. The extent of ozone depletion is greater over the south polar region than in the Arctic because

x   a.   the mechanism of ozone depletion requires sunlight and very cold temperatures.
      b.   Antarctica is in the path of prevailing winds that carry ozone-depleting substances into the stratosphere.
      c.   Antarctica has a longer winter, the time during which the most severe ozone depletion takes place.
      d.   All of the above are true.

8. The brief period of very rapid cooling and subsequent warming that occurred at the end of the last glaciation is called the

      a.   Little Ice Age.
x   b.   Younger Dryas Event.
      c.   Holocene Epoch.
      d.   Pleistocene-Pliocene boundary.

9. Maximum concentrations of ozone are found in a layer between _____ and _____ km above the Earth's surface.

      a.   0, 10
      b.   5, 15
x   c.   25, 35
      d.   50, 75

10. Domestic livestock, especially cattle, are great producers of

    a. NO_2.
x   b. CH_4.
    c. O_3.
    d. CO_2.

11. The passage of material through the biosphere is so rapid that the entire content of CO_2 in the atmosphere cycles every

    a.   4.5 days.
    b.   4.5 months.
x   c.   4.5 years.
    d.   45 years.

12. Which one of the following is not an important reservoir for carbon dioxide in the Earth system?

    a.   calcium carbonate shells of aquatic organisms
    b.   coal deposits
    c.   limestone
x   d.   clay-rich soils

13. The rate at which natural processes are removing carbon dioxide from the atmosphere is _____ the rate at which human activities are adding it.

x   a.   slower than
    b.   faster than
    c.   approximately the same as
    d.   not comparable to

14. Water vapor accounts for about _____ percent of the natural greenhouse effect.

    a.   20
    b.   40
    c.   60
x   d.   80

15. _____ contributes significantly to the annual observed increase in atmospheric CO_2.

       a.   The burning of fossil fuels
       b.   Widespread deforestation
       c.   The use of wood as a primary fuel in many developing countries
x   d.   All of the above are true.

16. Which one of the following is not one of the changes that scientists predict will be associated with global climatic warming?

       a.   shifting of forest boundaries in response to altered temperature and precipitation patterns
x   b.   global decrease in sea levels due to excess evaporation
       c.   increased droughts in some midcontinental agricultural regions
       d.   All of the above are changes that scientists predict will be associated with global climatic warming.

17. Which one of the following is not one of the changes that scientists predict will be associated with global climatic warming?

       a.   enhanced rates of soil decomposition
x   b.   warmer and drier conditions throughout the world
       c.   changes in global ice cover, comprising growth of ice cover in some circumstances and reduction in others
       d.   All of the above are changes that scientists predict will be associated with global climatic warming.

18. GCM stands for

       a.   general climate model.
x   b.   general circulation model.
       c.   global climate moderation.
       d.   global climatic mean.

19. Sea level increases resulting from global climatic warming will result from

       a.   the expansion of ocean water.
       b.   meltwater from shrinking glaciers.
       c.   increased calving along the margins of tidewater glaciers and ice sheets.
x   d.   All of the above are true.

20. Most climate models predict that, with no further additions, the anthropogenically generated greenhouse gases <u>already</u> in the atmosphere would cause an average global temperature increase of

x   a.   0.5 to 1.5°C.
      b.   1.5 to 4.5°C.
      c.   5 to 10°C.
      d.   0.1 to 0.2°C.

II.   Fill-Ins

1. Maximum concentrations of ozone are found in a layer between _____ and _____ km above the Earth's surface.

   (25...35)

2. In Costa Rica, forests covered _____ percent of the country in 1940, but by 1983 the amount of forested land had been reduced to _____ percent.

   (67...17)

3. The long wavelength radiation near the surface of the Earth by atmospheric gases is called _ _____ .

   (the greenhouse effect)

4. A short period of unusually rapid cooling and subsequent warming, called the _____ , occurred in North America and Europe at the end of the last glaciation.

   (Younger Dryas)

5. Land degradation due to human impacts in arid regions may lead to _____ .

   (desertification)

6. The belt of semi-arid lands bordering the southern edge of the Sahara desert is called the _____ .

   (Sahel)

7. Shelled aquatic organisms provide a reservoir for carbon dioxide by building their shells out of _____ .

    ($CaCO_3$) or (calcium carbonate)

8. Any atmospheric gas that is present only at very low concentration, measurable in parts per billion by volume (ppbv), is called a _____ gas.

    (trace)

9. Three-dimensional mathematical models of the Earth's climate system, called _____ , attempt to link atmospheric, hydrospheric, and biospheric processes in order to simulate the general character of present-day climates and predict future trends.

    (general circulation models) or (GCMs)

10. _____ are ice-like solids in which gas molecules, mainly methane, are locked up in water trapped in ocean sediments and beneath frozen ground.

    (Gas hydrates)

III. Definitions

1. deforestation: the process of forest clearing.

2. desertification: the invasion of desert into nondesert areas.

3. greenhouse effect: the property of the Earth's atmosphere by which long wavelength heat rays from the Earth's surface are trapped or reflected back by the atmosphere.

IV. True-False Questions

1. Atmospheric ozone is decreasing at all latitudes outside the tropics. (T)

2. Even if all production of CFCs were to stop, a recovery to natural conditions in the ozone layer would likely take a century or more. (T)

3. The rate of lithospheric plate motion generally ranges from 1 to 12 mm/yr. (F)

4. Selenium is a naturally occurring element that can be toxic if consumed in sufficient quantity. (T)

5. Desertification results strictly from natural causes, such as extended periods of drought. (F)

6. An estimated 12 percent of the Amazonian rain forest has already been cleared. (T)

7. CFC-12 has 25 times the capacity of carbon dioxide to trap ultraviolet radiation near the Earth's surface. (F)

8. CFCs are greenhouse gases, in addition to being harmful to the ozone layer. (T)

9. When ozone occurs in the troposphere, it is a greenhouse gas. (T)

10. Most global temperature curves are reconstructed primarily from land stations located mainly in the northern hemisphere. (T)

11. Curves showing average annual temperature variations since the middle or late nineteenth century differ in detail, but they all show one characteristic feature: a long-term decrease in temperature during the past century. (F)

12. The increase in temperature associated with global climatic change will be essentially uniform throughout the world. (F)

13. In Africa, nearly 60% of forest clearing is related to fuelwood production. (T)

V. Short-Answer Questions

1. Why is the ozone hole more pronounced over the South Pole than over the North Pole?

Answer: The process of breaking down ozone molecules requires sunlight and very cold temperatures, both of which are present in the south polar region. In the Arctic, the period of critical spring conditions is much shorter.

2. Draw a neat, well-labelled diagram illustrating the greenhouse effect in the Earth's atmosphere.

Answer: (See Fig. 18.8 in the text.)

3. Describe the natural atmospheric processes by which a balance is created among O, O_2, and O_3.

Answer: In the ozone layer, ultraviolet radiation interacts with molecules of oxygen (O_2) , breaking them into two oxygen atoms (O), which are then able to combine with other O_2 molecules to form molecules of ozone (O_3). The ozone is in turn broken down by ultraviolet radiation, thereby creating a steady-state or balance among O, O_2, and O_3.

4. How do CFCs interfere with the natural balance in the ozone layer?

Answer: As CFCs rise into the upper atmosphere, ultraviolet radiation breaks them down, releasing chlorine. It is chlorine, in the form of chlorine monoxide (ClO), that does the damage: the chlorine atoms destroy the ozone, with each chlorine being capable of destroying as many as 100,000 ozone molecules before other chemical reactions remove the chlorine from the atmosphere.

5. What are the most obvious symptoms of desertification?

Answer: The most obvious symptoms include crop failures or reduced yields; reduction in rangeland biomass available to livestock; reduction in fuelwood supplies; reduction in water supplies resulting from decreased streamflow or a depressed groundwater table; advance of dune sand over agricultural lands; and disruption of life-support systems, leading to refugees seeking outside relief.

6. In what four reservoirs is carbon found in the Earth system, and in what form does it occur in each reservoir?

Answer: (1) as carbon dioxide in the atmosphere; (2) in organic compounds in the biosphere; (3) as dissolved carbon dioxide in the hydrosphere; and (4) in the calcium carbonate of limestone and in decaying and buried organic matter (peat, coal, and petroleum) in the lithosphere.

7. Why was Mauna Loa volcano in Hawaii chosen as a suitable site from which to carry out systematic measurements of atmospheric carbon dioxide?

Answer: The site was chosen because of its altitude and remote location far from sources of atmospheric pollution.

8. Methane gas is present in the atmosphere only at extremely low concentrations, yet it is considered to be one of the most important and worrisome greenhouse gases. Why?

Answer: Methane (CH_4) absorbs ultraviolet radiation 25 times more effectively than CO_2, making it an important greenhouse gas despite its low concentration in the atmosphere. Since the late 1960s, methane concentrations have increased at a rate of about 1 percent per year, and seems to be correlated with increases in population and certain human activities (growing rice, raising livestock).

9. What do scientists predict will be the response of soils to global climatic warming?

Answer: As temperature rises, the rate of decomposition of organic matter in soil will increase. Soil decomposition releases CO_2 to the atmosphere, thereby further enhancing the greenhouse effect.

VI.   Longer-Answer Questions, Essays & Critical Thinking Questions: Answers are not provided for these questions (because each student will formulate his or her answer differently), but page numbers for text references are given at the end of each question.

1. Describe how a combination of factors led to the concentration of toxic levels of selenium in wildlife in the Kesterson Reservoir in California. (p. 473-474)

2. Explain how overgrazing can lead to changes in the land surface, ultimately creating a positive feedback situation which contributes to desertification. (p. 476)

3. Explain how deforestation can upset the hydrological balance in a forested area. (477)

4. How can human activities change the natural balance in the carbon cycle? (p. 478-479)

5. Describe the two trends—seasonal and long-term—in carbon dioxide concentrations documented by studies at the Mauna Loa Observatory. (p. 481)